THE NATURALIST IN THE HEBRIDES

In the same series

THE NATURALIST IN CENTRAL SOUTHERN ENGLAND
by Derrick Knowlton

THE NATURALIST IN DEVON AND CORNWALL
by Roger Burrows

THE NATURALIST IN THE ISLE OF MAN
by Larch S. Garrad

THE NATURALIST IN LAKELAND
by Eric Hardy

THE NATURALIST IN LONDON
by John A. Burton

THE NATURALIST IN MAJORCA
by James D. Parrack

THE NATURALIST IN SCOTLAND
by Derrick Knowlton

THE NATURALIST IN SOUTH-EAST ENGLAND
by S. A. Manning

THE NATURALIST IN WALES
by R. M. Lockley

THE NATURALIST IN
The Hebrides

DERRICK KNOWLTON

DAVID & CHARLES
Newton Abbot   London   North Pomfret (VT)   Vancouver

TO ALAN WHO WAS A SON TO ME

ISBN 0 7153 7446 X
Library of Congress Catalog Card Number 77-076093

© Derrick Knowlton 1977

Set in 12 on 13pt Bembo
and printed in Great Britain
by Latimer Trend & Company Ltd
for David & Charles (Publishers) Limited
Brunel House Newton Abbot Devon

Published in the United States of America
by David & Charles Inc
North Pomfret Vermont 05053 USA

Published in Canada
by Douglas David & Charles Limited
1875 Welch Street North Vancouver BC

Contents

5

List of Illustrations

All photographs are from the author's collection

CHAPTER ONE

An outline of the region

*Topography—Climate—Origin and distribution
patterns of the flora and fauna—
Distinguished naturalists of the past*

TOPOGRAPHY

IN A HEAVILY POPULATED country such as the British Isles, remote
and sparsely inhabited areas are few indeed. One of the most
notable is the far-flung Hebridean archipelago off the western
coast of Scotland. There, more than 500 islands with their associated stacks and skerries stretch for 240 miles (386km) from the
headland of Rubha nan Leacan on Islay to the tip of the Fianuis
peninsula of North Rona. From west to east they span some 270
miles (434km) from the lonely stack of Rockall far out in the
Atlantic to the island of Seil linked with the mainland by the
'Bridge over the Atlantic'. From the air they look like detached
floating fragments of the mainland and that is really what they
are.

This is a land enveloped by the ocean, a region which has
always been the abode of seamen—primeval colonisers in
hollowed-out tree trunks and skin canoes, Roman voyagers in
war galleys, Irish saints in coracles, Norse rovers in longboats
and Scots fishermen today in trawlers. The sea dominates the
scene. Writing in the first century AD the great Roman historian
Tacitus commented: 'Nowhere hath the sea a greater dominion'.
Its waves have carved out the gigantic cliffs, created the raised

beaches, gouged out the caves and then, as a benign if somewhat capricious goddess, supplied the inhabitants with fertiliser, food and fruitful soil.

The smallness of the human population can be seen when comparison is made with an English county of about the same area; the population of the old West Riding of Yorkshire is approximately four million, that of the Hebrides under 46,000, although the rate of decline has slowed down in recent years. Their remoteness is well demonstrated by the fact that many maps do not show the Hebrides in their entirety since to do so would involve depicting what the old ballad describes as 'a waste of seas'. It is this large area of water which acts as a barrier and coupled with the absence of suitable landing sites prevents access to the small outlying rocky islands. Conversely, it is this water which provides the isolation and thus the attraction for the many people who are irresistibly drawn by the lure of islands.

This fascination is compounded of several ingredients: the enjoyment of the voyage; the satisfaction, in the case of the smaller islands, of being able to view the entire coastline and encompass it in a day's walking; a more mysterious, somewhat indefinable element of a Robinson Crusoe nature deriving from racial memories; and, perhaps the most important of all, there is in the Hebrides a way of life which is as different from that of sophisticated city existence as could be imagined. It is life stripped down to its essentials, untrammelled by the superfluities of modernity but rich in co-operation, courtesy, culture and hospitality combined with a great respect for nature and a reverence for its creator. When these contrasting cultures are weighed in the balance it is not the Hebridean way of life which is found wanting.

This book is concerned with the islands' plant and animal life and at this stage it is sufficient to mention that James Fisher, writing in 1948, described the Hebrides as the greatest natural treasure of the British Isles. This is no less true today. These Western Isles can be divided into three groups, the Inner and Outer Hebrides and a widely scattered collection of outlying

islands. The first two groups are separated in the south by the
Sea of the Hebrides and between Skye and the Uists by the
Little Minch. Between the Long Isle of Harris and Lewis and the
Scottish mainland is the Minch proper or North Minch.

The Inner Hebrides consist of a chain of islands 140 miles
(225km) long from Islay, Cara and Gigha in the south to Skye in
the north. Some are within a short distance of the mainland
coast whilst others lie well out in the Sea of the Hebrides. Most
of these islands resemble the mainland in their topography and
characteristic wildlife but a few are of Outer Hebridean type.
Three miles (4·8km) west of the Kintyre peninsula in the Sound
of Gigha lie the islands of Cara and Gigha. The former, though
only a mile (1·6km) long, used to be inhabited but today this
rather barren island is seal-haunted, overrun with bracken and of
interest chiefly for its herd of feral goats and coastal birds. Its
northern neighbour, Gigha, is considerably larger with a population of 140 and a greater appeal to the naturalist. A low, green
isle six miles (9·6km) long, its various habitats support a wealth
of wild flowers and its coastline together with the owner's noted
Achamore gardens provide breeding sites for numerous birds.

Farther to the west is the large island of Islay whose varied
rock types provide a miscellany of habitats. It is not an easy
island to describe. Many of its roads are surprisingly straight
and flat and only in the east does the land rise above a thousand
feet (304·8m). Yet its woods, lochs and cliffs are very beautiful
and the south-eastern part is particularly lovely with numerous
skerries offshore and wooded glens interspersed with green pastures. Above everything else, Islay is an island for the ornithol-
ogist with a total of bird species which would be considerable
for a mainland locality and which for a Hebridean island is
nothing short of remarkable. In winter the vast hordes of barnacle geese are everywhere on mudflats, salt marshes, pastures
and moorland and are one of the outstanding features of
Hebridean wildlife. About one-sixth of the world population
of this species winters on Islay and it has been suggested that
this may be the largest gathering of barnacle geese in the world.

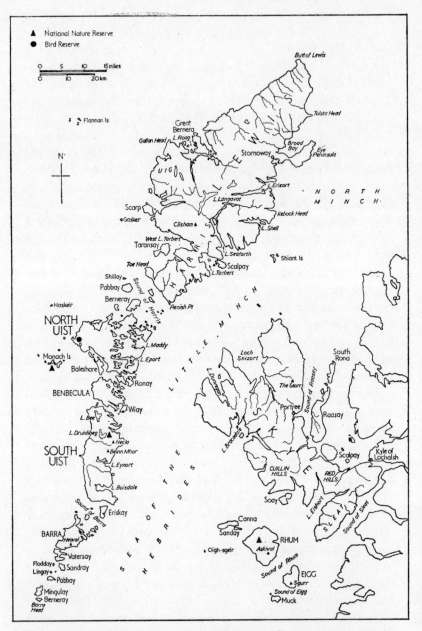

Fig 1 Map showing principal physical features and nature reserves of the northern Hebrides. Based upon the Ordnance Survey Map with the sanction of the Controller of HM Stationery Office (*Crown copyright reserved*)

The mountainous island of Jura, thirty miles (48km) long but relatively narrow, lies a mile (1·6km) to the north-east across the Sound of Islay and supplies a sharp contrast to its southern neighbour. Its appearance is largely determined by the uniform and barren nature of the Dalradian quartzite which covers most of the island resulting in monotonous moorland of a wild and desolate character. The southern half has a notable feature in the three Paps of Jura with their conspicuous quartzite screes. In clear weather they are visible for great distances and I have seen them from the summit of Ben Lawers in Tayside nearly eighty miles (129km) away; likewise from them in exceptional conditions the Isle of Man and the mountains of Donegal can sometimes be seen. The mountains attract a heavy rainfall which accentuates the feeling of desolation. In sunshine, the picture is very different and areas like Craighouse Bay, Tarbert and the western coast with its raised beaches and many caves are seen as the beautiful places they really are. If one goes to Islay for its birds, Jura is visited for its red deer which are exceedingly abundant and can be seen everywhere. When driving along the island's only road I passed three fine stags who decided to give me a race; they accelerated, overtook and passed in front of the car achieving a creditable speed in excess of 20mph (32kmph). Colonsay and Oronsay are linked by a tidal strand and really form one island situated eight miles (12·9km) west of Jura. It is a small and little known island of surpassing charm and despite its exposed position is rich in plant and bird life. North of Jura is a cluster of small isles ranging from hilly Scarba to the rocky Garvellochs and a group of former slate-quarrying islands abutting the mainland coast.

Moving north we come to Mull, the second largest island in the Inner Hebrides, lying athwart the Great Glen. Although it is twenty-five miles (40km) long and has a coastline of about 250 miles (402km), the population is only just over 2,000. Mull has typically Highland scenery with a central core of mountains and long sea lochs on the west coast. It is of outstanding scenic appeal and holds much to engross the geologist, apart from sea-

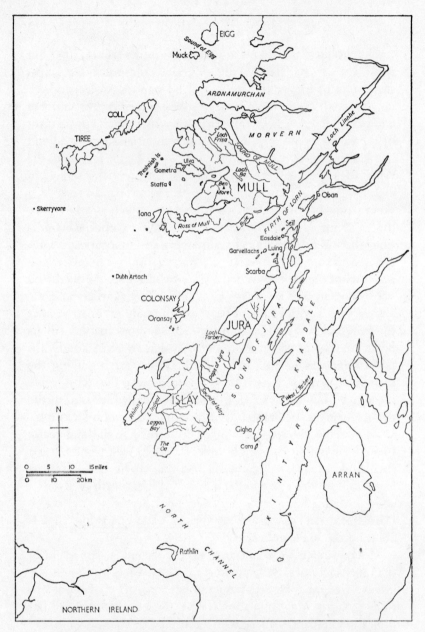

Fig 2 Map showing principal physical features of the southern Hebrides. Based upon the Ordnance Survey Map with the sanction of the Controller of HM Stationery Office (*Crown copyright reserved*)

bird colonies, eagles and a high buzzard population for the bird-watcher as well as rare moths for the entomologist. There are a number of islands off the western coast of Mull, notably Iona, Staffa, Ulva and the Treshnish Isles. All of these have much to engage the attentions of the nature lover; Iona with its marble, attractive serpentine pebbles and marine life, Staffa for its geological structure, Ulva with interesting butterflies and moths, and the Treshnish Isles, breeding grounds for Atlantic grey seals, shearwaters and storm petrels. West of the Treshnish Isles are situated the two medium-sized islands of Coll and Tiree, the former shaped like a huge fish swimming towards Ardna-murchan Point. Both are composed of Lewisian Gneiss and both contain interesting wildlife yet are possessed of very different scenery; Coll has much peaty moorland whilst Tiree being practically devoid of peat is largely rock and calcareous sand.

As one continues north, Argyllshire as it used to be known (now Strathclyde) is left behind and the Small Isles of Inverness-shire (now Highland) are reached, a heterogeneous group of five main islands, Muck, Eigg, Rhum, Sanday and Canna. Muck, a small and not very well known island, largely consists of basalt which produces a fertile soil. Underlying this are fossil-bearing Upper Jurassic strata which outcrop in one or two places. Though not by any means without interest for the naturalist es-pecially in its marine life it does not hold the attractions of its neighbours. Eigg, the nearest of these, is considerably larger and rises to well over twice the height of Muck. The scenery is more varied with a number of plantations and the so-called Singing Sands of Cleadale are well known. It is a good bird island and wild flowers abound. The summit of the Scuir gives a superb view of the southern sections of the Inner and Outer Hebrides. Geologically, Rhum is the odd one out for whilst the others are chiefly basalt it has a varied structure including much igneous rock some of which is of an uncommon type. The island was acquired in 1957 by the Nature Conservancy as a National Nature Reserve; it is the subject of numerous studies and is being used for research into land use and the development of maximum variety of flora and fauna so that guidance can be given in the formulation of management plans for other Highland reserves. The Sound of Canna washes the north-western shores of Rhum and across this sound lies the island of that name. A tidal strand links it with the low-lying island of Sanday. Here are basaltic land forms again and Canna has the fertile soil and typical plateaux with steep cliffs supporting strong seabird colonies and an interesting invertebrate fauna. The island is divided by a low-lying neck of land at Tarbert and the profile is easily seen from the north-western cliffs of Skye.

Skye is by far the largest of the Inner Hebrides and in sunshine holds many scenes of beauty but the appellation of the misty isle was not given without reason for the mountains attract heavy rainfall. So far as the naturalist is concerned the island's principal assets lie in its rare alpine flora and in the very varied rock structure which in some localities is of a quite bizarre nature. It has no distinctive wildlife and considering the size of its coastline and its tremendous cliffs it is remarkably deficient in nesting seabirds. A line of islands, of which Raasay is the largest, is situated between Skye and the mainland. Raasay is endowed with luxuriant vegetation due to its sheltered position and it is exceptionally well wooded for a Hebridean island. Rhododendrons give spectacular splashes of colour in the early summer. There are numbers of well kept cottages and altogether it is an exceedingly pleasant island. The flat topped hill of Dun Caan is a most conspicuous landmark from Skye and the mainland enabling the disorientated traveller easily to check his position. The island has a wealth of flowers including alpines, rich invertebrate life including rare moths, an endemic form of bank vole and several resident pairs of eagles.

The Outer Hebrides, 135 miles (217km) long, differ considerably from the Inner Hebrides; in their exposed position they have to bear the brunt of the Atlantic's fury and the savage onslaught of winds which on occasion break recording instruments. Consequently they are relatively bleak and barren. For the naturalist their interest, which is considerable, centres chiefly on the birdlife, the phytogeography of the plants and the zooge-ography of the invertebrates. The southernmost island is Berne-ray which lies on a latitude running between Coll and Muck. Together with its neighbour Mingulay it has outstanding bird cliffs. The nearby populated island of Vatersay looks on a map like a piece of a jigsaw. This line of islands extends north to the larger island of Barra which holds much of natural history interest especially in the machair and marine life. Beinn Eoligarry in the northern part provides a good viewpoint from which to see the Inner Hebrides and the mainland mountains.

If the machair is prominent on Barra it is even more so on South Uist where the calcareous lochs contain rare aquatics and have uncommon birds. The remote and virtually trackless eastern part rises to over 2,000ft (610m) and the summit of Beinn Mhor in clear visibility is an excellent viewpoint giving sight of St Kilda and the Flannans in the far north-west, and the Scottish mainland in the east with most of the Hebrides between. Benbecula is situated between North and South Uist and would be more aptly named Mid Uist. From an aesthetic point of view this low-lying island has a limited appeal but the situation is rather different for the angler since the surface is so studded with well-stocked lochs that there appears to be almost as much water as land. The naturalist too will find rich aquatic and marine life and possibly the largest population of corncrakes per square mile in the British Isles.

Benbecula is linked by bridges both to South and North Uist. The latter island is approximately the same size as South Uist and considerably larger than Benbecula. It follows the same general pattern as the other islands with extensive machair on the west backed by crofting communities, served by good roads, and hilly moorland in the central and eastern parts in all com-prising a wide range of habitats. I do not recall ever experiencing a greater density of nesting birds than on the RSPB reserve at Balranald. From near here in clear weather St Kilda appears for short spells of time as two indistinct humps on the far horizon. A number of small islands lie at varying distances from this

B

western coast including the rock skerry of Causamul which is part of the Balranald reserve, the isolated rock of Haskeir some seven miles (11km) west of Hougharry and the five low sandy islands of the Monachs, uninhabited since 1942 and a National Nature Reserve since 1966. They possess a rich machair flora and good numbers of birds. Fulmars began to breed about 1947 in the abandoned dwellings; there are both common and arctic terns and a breeding population of about 1,000 pairs of shags.

The island-strewn Sound of Harris separates North Uist from Harris and Lewis. Although these two districts were in separate counties until the recent local government reorganisation they are part of one large island seventy-five miles (121km) long as the hoodie flies from Renish Point to the Butt of Lewis. They are fairly distinct, however, in their topography; Harris has a mountainous interior, especially in the northern part, and a magnificent sandy coastline whilst Lewis consists of a boggy moorland plateau and a coastline with many steep cliffs although here too in places there are extensive sand dunes. In the 2622ft (799m) Clisham, Harris has the highest hill in the Outer Hebrides. The largest loch is Loch Langavat in southern Lewis which is seven and a quarter miles (11·7km) long. The deepest loch is Loch Suainaval in western Lewis which is 219ft (67m) deep. There is much for the plant ecologist to study. The sea inlets of western Harris and the coast around Stornoway are good for waders; the Sound of Harris and the Eye peninsula in Lewis have many duck in winter; the moorlands though possessing a rather sparse birdlife have a number of uncommon species and the hills have golden eagles. A number of islands are situated off the coasts and the most important of these for the naturalist are the Shiants in the Minch with their seabirds and Gasker off the western coast of Harris, a major breeding station for the Atlantic grey seal.

The third section, the outlying islands, consists of a heterogeneous assortment of small islands ranging from the 1,575 acres (638 hectares) of Hirta to the smallest and most isolated of all, the stack of Rockall, 224 miles (360km) west of the Outer

Hebrides. They are widely scattered, stretching from Rockall to North Rona across 270 miles (434km) of an ocean which is often storm-tossed and they are the remotest, most inaccessible parts of the British Isles. Few naturalists have visited them and the difficulties of access are such that few are likely to be able to visit them in the future. The easiest to visit is St Kilda but only a very few people can stay there in any one year and then only when weather conditions are favourable. Despite their isolation it is hardly possible to omit a brief reference to these islands for their importance in the field of natural history is out of all proportion to their size. The effects on plant and animal life of extreme exposure, the endemic bird and mammal forms, the important breeding stations of the Atlantic grey seal, the immense seabird colonies and the rare breeding birds are all subjects of concern and interest to the biologist. It is highly significant that of this small number of islands and stacks no less than nine are included in National Nature Reserves.

Rockall is so small, a mere 83ft (25·2m) in width and so far out in the Atlantic that it was unknown to the vast majority of people until it became news in 1955 when political considerations of international law required its formal annexation by the Crown. This event took place on 21 September of that year with such ceremony as is possible on an almost unclimbable wave-washed rock. For more than a hundred years a few men of enquiring mind and intrepid spirit from time to time have effected a landing on this lump of granite, the first such visit being by a naval party in 1810. Its chief interest centres on the physiography in that the part above ground is just the visible tip of the vast submarine Rockall Bank which is a ridge on the ocean floor beyond the edge of the Continental Shelf. The sea area around Rockall is noted for its valuable fisheries. Various pelagic seabirds have been observed on and around the rock; common guillemots have been seen on the ledge but it is not certain that they have ever bred there.

Nearer the mainland by 184 miles (296km) are the islands and stacks of St Kilda, seven in all. They were created a National

Nature Reserve in 1957. Stac an Armin at 627ft (191m) is the highest stack in Britain and on the main island of Hirta the great granite cliff of Conachair rises 1,397ft (426m) to form the highest sea cliff in the British Isles. To all who love out of the way spots St Kilda has acquired a romantic aura and for naturalists it has compelling attractions in the distinctive St Kildan mammals and wren and the huge, long established seabird colonies; in particular it has what is probably the largest gannetry in the world on Boreray which also has the original and largest fulmar colony in Britain.

If St Kilda can cast a quixotic spell on its devotees the Flannan Isles have their historic mystery which, however, must be left to the students of maritime drama. For the student of natural history these islands can provide, as can St Kilda, the rarest British nesting seabird, Leach's fork-tailed petrel. The Seven Hunters, as the Flannans are popularly known, are spread-eagled in three groups in the Atlantic seventeen miles (27km) west of Lewis; the largest is Eilean Mor, a mere thirty-nine acres (15·8 hectares).

Forty miles (64km) north of Lewis is Sula Sgeir with its gannetry of over 5,000 pairs and other seabirds. It is half a mile (.804km) long, a narrow rock of Lewisian Gneiss largely devoid of soil but with the typical maritime plants wherever their roots can obtain a hold. It has a number of caves one of which forms a tunnel right through the island. The larger island of North Rona is about twelve miles (19km) east-north-east of Sula Sgeir and together they form a National Nature Reserve. It also has caves and the northern part of the island is a low flat-topped peninsula having the largest breeding station of Atlantic grey seals in the Hebrides. The island also has the largest colony of Leach's fork-tailed petrel.

CLIMATE

As might be expected in a region which is spread over a large area of ocean and possesses land surfaces ranging from skerries just above the waves to mountains over 3,000ft (914m) there is considerable variation in the type of weather experienced. If, however, a succinct generalisation were to be made using two words one could say 'wind' and 'cloud'. Yet this would give a very misleading picture of some localities and is, in any case, an over simplification even of the general scene.

The principal factors involved are the maritime aspect, the exposed conditions, the Drift from the Gulf Stream and the northern latitude. The climate of the British Isles as a whole is governed by their situation in the cool temperate zone on the western edge of Europe; they lie in the path of the prevalent westerlies. The position of the Hebrides on the far western margin of Britain therefore means that they experience in extreme form the consequences of the strong prevailing winds bringing rainfall from across a wide reach of sea.

Here and there, especially in the Inner Hebrides, there are a few sheltered places in plantations and valleys but in general there is little or no protection from the relentless winds. The Southerner who experiences in his home locality more than two or three days of gales often finds himself in a state of tension and irritability but the Hebridean crofter has had to accept strong winds as a fact of life and learn to live with them. The Outer Isles are in one of the regular tracks of the depressions which sweep in from the Atlantic but although westerly winds prevail, in recent years the Hebrides in common with the mainland have been experiencing long spells of northerly and easterly winds in spring and early summer. I once camped for a week on an uninhabited island and after carefully siting the tent to face away from the prevailing south-westerly wind found to my chagrin that in six days gale-force winds came from all points of the compass. In summer these winds can be a nuisance to the naturalist as sand grains blow into his eyes and equipment and as he finds it impossible to keep binoculars or telescope steady. The nature photographer in particular has problems with plants that are seldom still.

Yet the impression must not be left that there are no days of calm. During a fortnight in May spent on an Outer Hebridean island there was only one stormy day and the winds were light for the rest of the time even though I was camping on the machair of the exposed Atlantic coast. The winter is the time when gales reach maximum ferocity. The structure of the crofters' cottages tell the story with their squat appearance, thick walls and few windows, which are tiny and deeply recessed. At the Butt of Lewis winter winds reach gale-force one day in three. A wind force of 108mph (174kmph) was recorded one winter day on Tiree and when it is realised that this is exactly twice the velocity of a strong gale on the Beaufort Scale some impression will be gained of its force and fury. Even stronger gusts up to 129mph (209kmph) were experienced on St Kilda in January 1962. The violence of the winter storms at Barra Head on Berneray at the southern tip of the Outer Hebrides has been mentioned in a number of books but the incredible effects are worth referring to again. Sir Archibald Geikie was the first to place on record the shifting by 5ft (1·5m) of a massive gneissose rock weighing forty-two tons (42·7 tonnes). At this same spot fish have been thrown upwards more than 600ft (183m) in the air to land on the cliff top. Such happenings as these have to be witnessed before the mind can fully comprehend the tremendous power behind them.

The prevailing westerlies ensure that cloud cover is often extensive even if rain does not always materialise. Yet the Hebrides have glorious days, especially in the early part of the summer when there is hardly a cloud in the sky and landscape photographers bewail the absence of those masses of cumuli which are essential to any self-respecting scenic shot. Moreover, the situation is not the same on every island; Iona often escapes the storm clouds which gather round the Ben More massif on Mull, and the low island of Tiree, awash in the waves, has an outstanding sunshine record. During early summer the amount of sunshine approaches that of South Coast resorts, often averaging eight hours daily in May and June. The changeable nature of British weather is proverbial, but whereas for much of Britain this is often on a daily basis for the Hebrides, as indeed for the north-west Scottish mainland, this variability must be thought of in hourly terms.

Amounts of rainfall vary not only from island to island but also within each island. The average annual rainfall of Tiree is 40in (102cm); of Iona 48in (122cm); much of both the Inner and Outer Isles have a range of 40–60in (102–152cm); the more hilly parts have between 60–80in (152–203cm) and only small areas of the Cuillins of Skye and the mountains of mid-Mull reach 125in (317cm) equalling that on the mountains of the western mainland. There is considerable variation also on individual islands. On Mull, for example, the tip of the Ross of Mull has about 50in (127cm); the foot of the volcanic complex and the south-east about 80in (203cm); the north-east 90in (228cm) and the summits of the mountains 125in (317cm). On Lewis records show 39·5in (100cm) at Stornoway on the north-east coast; 48in (122cm) at Shawbost on the north-west coast; 62in (157cm) at Gisla in the south-west; the last amount is virtually doubled at Loch Askavat with 123·7in (314cm). The wettest part of Jura is the eastern side which on the face of it is a little surprising since this is in the lee of the Paps but the reason probably lies in the narrow width of the island and the fact that the eastern coast is too close to the hills to come within the rain shadow area.

On the credit side there are not usually more than two or three days in the year when thunder occurs and there is very little frost or snow. That frost and snow are rare is a fact not realised by many people who equate the Hebrides with the Central Highlands on the naïve basis that both regions are situated in the far north of Britain. They do not take into account the far-reaching influence of the North Atlantic Drift which is an extension of the Gulf Stream currents. Several of the Inner Isles such as Colonsay, Muck and Canna can produce first early potatoes before the market gardens of Southern England. The northern latitude gives long summer days in the northern half of the region and conversely brief winter hours of daylight. The Hebridean climate also resembles that of the north-west mainland coastal areas in its equable nature with an annual temperature range of only 14° F (10° C) from 41° F (6° C) in winter to 55° F (13° C) in summer. The low summer temperature, high cloud cover and strong winds undoubtedly deter numbers of potential holidaymakers. The relatively small but growing body of visitors who have succumbed to the esoteric charms of the Hebrides not only know that its climate is unjustly maligned but also that, in any event, its treasures heavily outweigh such climatic disadvantages as may arise.

ORIGIN AND DISTRIBUTION PATTERNS OF THE FLORA AND FAUNA

For a number of reasons the Hebrides have exercised a magnetic influence on many a naturalist in the past and this allure is still as potent as ever. The beauty and distinctiveness of the Hebridean scene—the machair starry with flowers, the whitewashed cottages deeply rooted on their crofts, the stupendous cliffs, the seas of malachite green and the wide expanse of shell–sand beaches—make the power of the magnet plain.

Perhaps more than most people the naturalist feels an exhilarating lifting of his spirit when he comes to a region where human influence on nature, though not inconsiderable, is less than in most other places and this is certainly true of the Hebrides with their low population, geographic isolation and negligible industry. Then, too, the distinctive oceanic fauna in all its wild abundance is a justification for his excited interest. A more specialised claim on his attention is the existence of island sub-species in some of the animals. Lastly, the peculiar distribution of some of the plants and animals—the phytogeography and zoogeography of the scientist—makes a rewarding study for the enquiring mind.

The composition and distribution of the Hebridean flora and fauna set many problems for which there are no easy answers. Various hypotheses have been postulated but these are not matters about which anyone can be dogmatic since in the very nature of the case, cast-iron proof is hardly possible. The manner in which the islands were formed is described in the next chapter. The resultant isolation inevitably had a profound effect on the composition of the wildlife. The very remoteness of some of the smaller islands has enabled the Atlantic grey seals to breed and the rarer petrels to nest.

A notable effect of isolation is the evolution of distinct island races in some birds, mammals, insects and plants although in some cases it is only in the Outer Isles that separate sub-species have evolved. For good measure the wren exists in three subspecies in the region—the typical form in the Inner Isles and the forms *hebridensis* in the Outer Isles and *hirtensis* on St Kilda. The situation in the Inner Hebrides is not entirely clear for Skye and Raasay have wrens which are considered to be intermediate in character between the mainland and Outer Hebridean forms. Another bird whose sub-specific status is uncertain is the dipper; Baxter and Rintoul (1953) consider that those on Mull and Skye are probably the mainland form and that all other islands have the Irish race. Another member of that country's fauna occurs in the Outer Hebrides—the Irish form of the red grouse. The Hebridean rock pipit is found only in the Outer Isles and on St Kilda. The form *hebridensis* of the song thrush which is found on the Outer Isles is recorded from Skye, and probably also occurs on Raasay. It is rather strange that Skye which is so near the mainland should have faunistic links with the Outer Isles, but this doubtless is due to the mobility of birds for in general Skye's wildlife pattern resembles that of the mainland. The Shetland starling var *zetlandicus* also occupies the Outer Hebrides including St Kilda but it is said that only young birds can be separated in the field. Other birds with Hebridean races are the stonechat and hedge-sparrow both of which also breed on parts of the western mainland. All these island forms tend to a darker or more intense coloration.

There are as yet some unresolved problems of distribution for it will have been noticed that there is no clear-cut pattern. Some birds are found only in the outer archipelago, others in both

Outer and Inner Hebrides whilst a third group occur also on the mainland. Why, for example, should there be a Hebridean song thrush but not a missel thrush? The answer in this case may be because the latter bird was a later arrival and exists only in small numbers in the Outer Hebrides, but much more puzzling is why there should be a Hebridean rock pipit and not a meadow pipit when both are common and have long been present.

The effect of isolation on mammals has been different from that on birds in that due to the former's relative lack of mobility they have often evolved into separate forms on individual islands. There is, however, an alternative theory that the earliest small mammal immigrants from the Continent reached the islands remaining relatively pure stock whilst those which came later and remained on the mainland have evolved into separate races. A small sub-species of stoat has developed on Islay and Jura and has been named *Mustela erminae ricinae* to differentiate it from the mainland stoat *M. e. stabilis* which is found on a few of the other Inner Hebridean islands. The form *ricinae* is not noticeably smaller in the field as I discovered when I watched one hunting in a disused quarry on Islay. This island has a distinct form of the common shrew *Sorex araneus granti* in which the belly coloration extends higher up the flanks than in the mainland animals. Islay also has a sub-species of short-tailed vole with a short, dark coat which has been named *Microtus agrestis macgillivraii* after William McGillivray, the famous Scottish naturalist.

This mammal, more than any other, has differentiated into a number of island forms. All the Hebridean forms, unlike those of Orkney, have originated directly or indirectly from the sub-species *M. a. neglectus* which at the present time occupies the Scottish Highlands. Most of the islands have the Hebridean race *M. a. exsul*. As already mentioned, Islay has a separate sub-species and Gigha and Eigg each have a sub-species named *M. a. fiona* and *M. a. mial* respectively which like that of Islay have evolved from *exsul* whilst Muck has a sub-species *M. a. luch* which is considered to have developed directly from the Highland race. For a fuller account of the origin of the small mammals the reader is referred to Dr L. Harrison Matthew's book *British Mammals*.

The bank vole is only known to occur on two Hebridean islands and both populations have evolved into sub-species which have probably developed from the original species invading Britain at the end of the Ice Age rather than from the mainland bank vole of the present day which is smaller and lighter-coloured. Mull has *Clethrionomys glareolus alstoni* and Raasay *C. g. erica*, the latter being the larger of the two.

Most Hebridean islands have the sub-species *hebridensis* of the long-tailed field mouse *Apodemus sylvaticus*. On a number of the islands the mice have slight differences in some physical characteristics but opinions differ regarding the desirability of granting sub-specific status. The form *hirtensis* living on St Kilda may well be justified in possessing this rank for it has been isolated on this remote island for a very long period of time. Recent research has shown that genetically it resembles the mice of Norway rather than those of the British mainland which may mean that this species was introduced by the Vikings. It is generally agreed that the field mouse found on Skye belongs to the mainland race and this may be taken as an indication that this island has only separated from the mainland in relatively recent times. St Kilda once possessed its own race of house mouse *Mus musculus muralis* of richer coloration than the type. It became known as the Post Office mouse because the colony lived in and around this building but only a small number remained at the time of the evacuation in 1930 and they became extinct not many months later. This mouse resembled more those from the Faeroes rather than the race on the British mainland.

Amongst the invertebrates there are quite a number of island races notably in the butterflies and moths. The situation is different from that of the small mammals for unlike them the Hebridean forms of some butterflies co-exist with the typical race on the same island and there is no insular variety which is restricted to one island. It is a puzzling fact that while some butterflies have relatively quickly responded to geographical isolation others show no variation at all. The meadow brown *Maniola jurtina* occurs in the typical race on a number of islands but a distinctly brighter variety dignified with the name *splendida* flies in parts of the western mainland and in the Outer Hebrides on Vatersay, Barra, South Uist and the small island of Baleshare lying just off the western coast of North Uist. The last named is an extremely localised population since so far as is known it does not occur on North Uist. The marsh fritillary *Euphydryas aurinia* is interesting in that the Irish sub-species *praeclara*, or at least a form closely resembling it, is recorded from Rhum, Tiree, the small island of Gunna to the north of Tiree, Islay and Jura; this of course is indicative of former land connections with Ireland. A large form of the dark green fritillary *Argynnis aglaia scotica* flies in the Outer Isles except in North Uist, Harris and Lewis; in the Inner Hebrides this large form has been noted on Rhum and South Rona. A third fritillary, the small pearl-bordered *A. selene*, exists in the race *insularum* on Rhum, Skye and some of its attendant isles. The large heath *Coenonympha tullia* is well distributed throughout the region in the form *scotica* with indistinct eye spots and a lighter colour than the typical race. E. B. Ford has stated that this latter race is not uncommon on Islay although the northern sub-species is more plentiful. In this butterfly we see a reversal of the usual trend in Hebridean sub-species which is generally towards a darker coloration.

Several moths have distinct Hebridean races. The yellow shell *Euphyia bilineata*, a common moth of pastures, exists in a small dark-coloured form *atlantica*. The tiny red-mottled foxglove pug whose caterpillars live inside foxglove flowers has the variety *hebudium* in which the red colour is replaced by dark brown and white. The third example is perhaps the most interesting. The belted beauty *Nyssia zonaria* is a most attractive moth with a white background on which is superimposed a pattern of dark lines from which its vernacular name derives. It has a strange discontinuous distribution occurring along the coasts of North Wales and north-west England, in parts of Ireland and on the sand dunes of the Hebrides where it has evolved into the race *atlantica*.

Of other insects the eleven-spot ladybird beetle *Coccinella 11-punctata*, which is of similar colour pattern to the familiar seven-spot ladybird but rather smaller and with five spots on each elytra instead of three, has developed into a distinct variety *boreolitoralis*. The heath bumble bee *Bombus jonellus* has been differentiated into the variety *hebridensis* and the typical bumble bee of the machair *Bombus smithianus* is regarded by some authorities as being merely a larger form of *B. muscorum*.

Several common plants found in the Hebrides have sufficiently distinct characteristics to be designated sub-species. One such is known as the Hebridean orchid *Dactylorhiza fuchsii hebridensis* which is a dwarf form of the spotted orchid. The pyramidal orchid *Anacamptis pyramidalis* is much less common in northern Britain but it is found in the Hebrides in what J. W. Heslop-Harrison regarded as a distinct form. The common rose of the north, *Rosa sherardii*, has the variety *cookei* in the Hebrides and the honeysuckle of the Outer Isles has been differentiated as var *clarkii* after the botanist W. A. Clark.

Apart from the evolution of island races the Hebrides have an astonishing cosmopolitan medley of plants and animals from the British mainland, the Arctic, the Alps, Ireland, America, the Lusitanian region and even one plant with an extraordinary discontinuous distribution in West Africa and China. The least carpet moth *Sterrha rusticata* occurs in Britain only on St Kilda, in south-east England and in a few other well-dispersed localities on the coast of southern England.

Like the Scottish mainland, the more mountainous islands have a generous quota of relict arctic/alpine plants and animals. The alpines include two that are not known from mainland Britain; the basaltic area of the Storr on Skye has *Koenigia islandica* and, also on Skye, the Cuillins provide a home for the alpine rock-cress *Arabis alpina*. With the exception of St Kilda the islands were heavily glaciated but it is possible that alpines survived in a few areas which were free from ice such as ledges along the coast and summits rising above the ice which are known as nunataks. An alternative possibility is that some of the plants have migrated from ice-free land now beneath the sea west of the Outer Isles. A few insect species whose normal habitat is either the Arctic tundras or the high Alps exist as glacial relics and these include several water beetles such as *Dytiscus lapponicus*, *Agabus arcticus*, *Deronectes assimilis* and the surface-dwelling *Gyrinus opacus*.

A number of Irish plants and animals live on some of the islands. Coll is the most important island in this respect but others include Tiree, Gunna, Colonsay, Islay and the Uists. Two orchids from Ireland are the Irish ladies' tresses *Spiranthes romanzoffiana* which grows on Coll and Colonsay and the Irish marsh orchid *Orchis occidentalis* which is found on Coll and Tiree. An aquatic of rather odd appearance is the rare pipewort *Eriocaulon septangulare* which grows on Coll, Skye and Scalpay. Another less rare but still uncommon aquatic is the flexible naiad *Naias flexilis* of lochs on Colonsay, Islay and the Uists. A non-flowering constituent of the Hebridean vegetation is an Irish moss *Campylopus shawii*. Several lochs on Barra hold an Irish and American freshwater sponge *Heteromyenia ryderi* and it has been recorded from a number of other islands in the Outer Hebrides.

The Irish or transparent burnet moth *Zygaena purpuralis* with horizontal bars on the forewings instead of the more typical spots can be seen in flight in the southern part of Mull, on Eigg, Rhum and the tiny island of Gunna in the strait between Coll and Tiree. The Irish race of the marsh fritillary has been mentioned earlier. The distribution pattern of these plants and animals is by no means simple but it is strongly indicative of land links with Ireland in the geologically recent past and is consistent with the theory that Coll and Tiree were still joined to Ireland after the Outer Hebrides had been separated.

A further complication is that some of these Irish plants and animals are also of American occurrence. The possibility of an ancient link with the New World via Greenland is strengthened by the existence in the Hebrides of species of more direct American origin. An exciting find in a South Uist loch during 1943 was the pondweed *Potamogeton epihydrus*, an American species not previously known from the British Isles. Two American molluscs have been recorded, one from the Inner and one from the Outer Hebrides; *Planorbis dilatata*, a tiny trumpet snail whose flat shell is only 3mm in diameter was discovered on Raasay and *Clausilia craven-sis* on Harris and North Uist. In 1973 nine specimens of the American wainscot moth *Mythimisa unipuncta* appeared on Canna but these must have been migrants.

As well as this western fauna and flora there are the plants and animals of the Pyrenees, the Mediterranean and the Atlantic islands of Madeira, the Azores and the Canaries. The Hebridean moss *Myurium hebridarium* is an oceanic type which, though rare, is abundant in some localities in its characteristic habitat of ledges on sea cliffs. It is a strongly growing moss of yellow green colour well distributed throughout the Outer Isles and occurring also on Canna, Rhum, Coll and Tiree. Apart from the Hebridean stations and two localities on the Scottish mainland it is found only in the Atlantic islands listed above.

Professor Heslop-Harrison has suggested that the Hebridean moss is a remnant of the Tertiary flora but on the other hand W. A. Clark considered that it is probably a post-glacial arrival. There is thus no general agreement amongst botanists regarding their origin and in the nature of the case there is not likely to be.

The most extraordinary instance of abnormal plant distribution must surely be that of the moss *Bartramidula wilsoni* which grows on South Uist and Harris, in a few localities on the mainland, in a relatively small area of West Africa adjoining the Gulf of Guinea and in the mountainous area of Yunnan in South China. It seems futile even to attempt to speculate on the origin of this one.

Three water beetles of the Lusitanian region inhabit certain waters. An exciting event in 1936 was the discovery by a Durham University expedition of a whirligig beetle new to

Britain in a small Raasay loch. It has subsequently been located
in another loch on Baleshare island off the western coast of
North Uist. This was *Aulonogyrus striatus* a surface-dwelling
beetle like the rest of the Gyrinids but differing from them in the
broad yellow margins of the thorax and wing-cases. This is a
beetle of the Canary Islands and of the Mediterranean and its
appearance in one or two isolated Hebridean stations so far from
its main breeding area is remarkable. An equally notable event
was the coincidental finding of another Canary Island species in
a small loch on Barra in the previous year. This was the small
water beetle *Deronectes canariensis* again new to the British list.
The third beetle is a tiny Pyrenean species *Hydroporus foveolatus*
discovered in a small peaty lochan on one of the mountains of
Rhum. These species may have spread northwards from the
Mediterranean at the end of the Ice Age before the Irish Sea came
into existence. Another possibility is that these Lusitanian species
like the arctic/alpines survived the glaciations in a few favoured
places.

If some species survived the glaciations and others migrated
over land bridges a few creatures arrived by swimming, others
by flight and some were deliberately introduced by man. Otters
are mammals who have obviously arrived in the islands via the
surrounding seas. The presence of the fox on Skye is probably
due to the island's proximity to the mainland making it well
within the animal's swimming capacity. Skye is the only place in
the Hebrides where the fox now exists but it is known to have
lived on Mull in the seventeenth century, an island to which it
probably came by crossing the Sound of Mull. Boswell recorded
a solitary fox on Raasay in 1772 which he said must have been
introduced, but a fox could swim to Raasay as well as to Skye.
Deer did not generally colonise the islands by swimming to
them but in a few instances they have augmented stock by crossing from neighbouring islands in this way, for example, from
Jura to Islay, in the Sound of Harris, where they are known to
swim from Pabbay to North Uist, and in the Sound of Mull
where they swim to that island from the mainland. The pine

Plate 1 (above) Fingal's Cave, Staffa with its outstanding columns of basalt
Plate 2 (below) Old Man of Storr, Skye, another basaltic rock

Plate 3 (above) Barnacle geese on Islay
Plate 4 (below) Perhaps the most numerous butterfly in the Hebrides; the common blue butterfly on Mull

marten which was reported from Raasay in 1971 must have negotiated the Inner Sound.

Seas constitute no problem to birds and the breeding populations of the isles established themselves at the end of the Ice Age. Nevertheless the islands in general have an impoverished bird fauna compared with the mainland and the smaller and more distant islands have the lowest number of species. The range and extent of suitable habitat is less and in the main it is only when a build-up of population takes place that the birds concerned are driven to seek fresh nesting areas elsewhere. Yet the colonising of the Hebrides by birds was not a once-for-all process but a continuing one as new habitats are formed and as population explosions take place. Examples of this are the arrival of the coal and long-tailed tits as breeding species in Lewis in 1963 and the colonisation of many islands by the collared dove in the 1960s. Dr David Lack noted in 1942 that 19 out of 75 land and fresh-water birds of the Outer Hebrides had arrived there since 1800. Another characteristic of Hebridean bird populations pointed out by Dr Lack is their erratic fluctuations. This is due in part to the smallness of individual populations which can easily become, at least temporarily, extinct.

Several mammal species have been the subject of introductions. Fresh stocks of red deer have been taken to a number of islands either to augment the existing population or to establish them for the first time. For example, introductions were made in the nineteenth century to Jura, Scalpay and Raasay in the Inner Hebrides and North Uist, Pabbay and South Harris in the Outer Hebrides; in the present century more deer have been taken to Rhum. Fallow deer were probably taken to Islay as early as the fourteenth century and much later to Scarba, Mull, Cara and Rhum, although they are now extinct on three of these. Early introductions of roe deer were also made to Islay but in the few other islands where they occur their arrival could well have been by swimming from the mainland.

Rabbits were introduced at various times in the Middle Ages on a number of islands and later even to some of the remote

C

stacks by lighthouse keepers. Hares, both mountain and brown, have been brought into a number of islands for sport. Hedgehogs are known to have been introduced to Skye just before the beginning of the present century and have now become widespread; they occur on several of the other Inner Isles where doubtless they were also introduced. Some mammals have been inadvertantly brought by man, the classic example being the rat whose ship populations sometimes swarm ashore and rapidly establish breeding colonies. No rats were known on Skye in the eighteenth century when Boswell and Johnson visited the island but these animals are there today. The brown rat is indeed all too common on many islands. The mole is another mammal which can be introduced by accident when soil is transported. It is not found in the Outer Hebrides but lives on a number of the Inner Isles. The date of its arrival in Mull is known for some were discharged with ballast from a ship in 1800.

DISTINGUISHED NATURALISTS OF THE PAST

The average population density of the Hebrides is seventeen persons per square mile (2·6 hectares) compared with 171 for Scotland and 916 for England. In view of this extremely low figure it is not really surprising that these islands have produced few outstanding naturalists in the past. Even William McGillivray, whose biographical details were given in the author's *The Naturalist in Scotland* and who was the Outer Isles' one great natural scientist with a childhood home on Harris, was born on the mainland at Aberdeen where he spent the major part of his life. Most of his studies, too, were carried out on the mainland.

In the Inner Hebrides is the birthplace of a man who might not have regarded himself as a naturalist but who was one of the first to compile painstaking records of the wildlife of the western islands among which he made extensive journeys at the end of the seventeenth century. His name was Martin Martin and he was born in Skye about the middle of that century, although the exact date is unknown. He was first a tutor to the son of MacDonald of Sleat and then to the son of Macleod of Dunvegan. Subsequently he became a qualified but non-practising physician who travelled in the Hebrides and later moved to London where he died in 1719. His *Description of the Western Islands of Scotland* published in 1703 gives an interesting and valuable account not only of the social customs of the people but also of the wildlife and is thus of great value in tracing the historical development of Hebridean ecology. He appears inclined to accept the islanders' statements at face value and it is necessary to differentiate between these, which include many superstitions, and his first-hand observations. He published a separate account of his expedition to St Kilda entitled *A Late Voyage to St Kilda*.

Apart from Martin the recorded study of Hebridean natural history was made by visiting naturalists although the present century has seen a few resident on the isles. The earliest detailed topographical description was a manuscript written by Sir Donald Monro who travelled throughout the Hebrides in 1549 on the instigation of the famous botanist, Sir Robert Sibbald. A voyage such as this at so early a date must have been hazardous in the extreme. Monro was known by the somewhat grandiose title of High Dean of the Isles; the significance of this term is obscure and it may well have been merely a courtesy title. Very little is known of his career except that he was a minister in Easter Ross and may also have had pastoral associations with the island of Lewis. His book, the first printed issue of which was made in 1774, is in the nature of a gazetteer of 207 islands. Some of his measurements are a little adrift and he placed Islay to the west of Lismore, confusing it with Mull; this was apparently a momentary aberration on his part for later on he describes Mull in its correct setting and all in all, considering the lack of facilities available in those times, he gives as accurate an account as can be expected. He not only notes the means of livelihood but also records the more conspicuous elements of nature; for example, he refers to the abundance of Solan geise (gannets) on Elsay

(Ailsa Craig), the fine forest for deire on Duray (Jura), the cockles on the Great Strand of Barra and the islands on which peregrines nest.

A very long interval elapsed before the visit of the next scribing naturalist, Thomas Pennant. He was born in 1726 in a village of North Wales and he died in the same village in 1798. It would be quite rash, however, to assume from this bald statement that he was parochial in his outlook for peripatetic would be a more fitting adjective with which to describe him. An earlier journey to the Scottish mainland in 1769 inspired him to make a return visit in 1772 which included an extensive tour of the Hebrides though not apparently to the Outer Isles. He was accompanied by the botanist the Rev John Lightfoot and by Moses Griffith the illustrator of his books. En route Pennant was presented with the Freedom of the City of Edinburgh. His book *A Tour in Scotland and Voyage to the Hebrides, 1772* was published in 1774.

Those inimitable literary twins James Boswell and Dr Samuel Johnson would be the last to describe themselves as naturalists and with good reason. They knew little and cared less about the wildlife of the British countryside; their concern was with books and people, especially social conversation. Yet even they could not be entirely immune from some of the facts of natural history when these were supplied by their hosts and in the best traditions of journalism these facts were faithfully reproduced in their diaries. It was in 1773 that Boswell and Johnson made their celebrated tour of a number of the Inner Hebrides. Unlike their predecessor Pennant, who wisely began his journey in May, they made their tour in the autumn and in consequence endured some atrocious weather and some uncomfortable, not to say, dangerous voyages. Possibly it was the weather which prejudiced them against some of the landscape although an equally likely reason is that they shared the prevailing tastes of the time. It is interesting to note the changes in popular preference for landscape types over the years and it is evident that the choice in the eighteenth century differed considerably from that of our own day. Then, approval was given to the strictly utilitarian ideal of profitable crops and to a picturesque arboriculture. The natural patterns of open countryside were not appreciated. So whilst in southern England William Cobbett was ranting against the wastes of Bagshot, Boswell and Johnson between them were declaiming against the horrible desert of the Coll sand dunes and the dreariness of Mull. The classification of heathland and dunes as areas of great natural beauty would be incomprehensible to them. They recorded details of the fish, mammals and birds particularly of Raasay, Skye and Coll and at Armadale in Skye they actually met and conversed with a naturalist from Aberdeenshire. How fascinating it would be to have an account of their conversation but regrettably this was one occasion when they failed to make a record.

We have to wait nearly sixty years for the next arrival. In 1831 the naturalist, G. C. Atkinson visited St Kilda and an account of his findings was subsequently published as part of the Transactions of the Northumberland Natural History Society. He was one of the earliest of a long succession of naturalists who paid fleeting trips to those remote islands in the nineteenth century. Among them was William MacGillivray's son John who went there in 1840. Another was J. A. Harvie-Brown who with colleagues wrote the first comprehensive accounts of the birds and mammals of the Western Isles in *A Vertebrate Fauna of the Outer Hebrides* in 1885 and *A Vertebrate Fauna of Argyll and the Inner Hebrides* in 1892. He was one of the very few people in that century, apart from Lewis men, who landed on Sula Sgeir and on North Rona (in 1887 and 1888 respectively). He initiated bird population surveys and obtained valuable information on bird migration from lighthouse keepers.

One of the earliest geologists to interest himself in the Hebrides was Dr John MacCulloch. His family originated from Galloway but he was born in Guernsey in 1773. He became a doctor of medicine but later transferred his attentions to geology. For many years he paid annual visits to Scotland including the Hebrides and in 1819 wrote *A Description of the Western Isles of*

Scotland. In addition to other books he contributed some seventy-nine articles, most of them on geology, to scientific journals. In 1826 the Government commissioned him to make a geological map of Scotland. This took him six years and he died following an accident shortly before its publication.

The 8th Duke of Argyll was an amateur geologist who in 1851 read a paper before the Geological Society of London on the leaf beds at Ardtun on the island of Mull. About this time J. D. Forbes of Pitsligo in Aberdeenshire who was a geophysicist with a special interest in glaciology was carrying out studies on the glaciation of Loch Coruisk in Skye. Sir Archibald Geikie, Director General of the Geological Survey, took a personal interest in the Hebrides and visited North Rona in 1894 and St Kilda in the two following years. Dr John Wilson Dougal was an amateur geologist of Edinburgh whose especial interest was in the flinty crush zone of the Lewisian Gneiss in the Long Island. In his search for the continuation of this zone he visited North Rona in 1927 and Sula Sgeir in 1930. Dr A. M. Cockburn was born in Edinburgh in 1901 and graduated in geology with first-class honours in 1924. In collaboration with J. Matthieson he produced for the Ordnance Survey the first six-inch map of the St Kilda group which was published in 1928. He spent some time on St Kilda in that year preparing with the painstaking accuracy for which he was noted a geological map which was published in 1935. He died in 1959. A. G. Steavenson, born in 1888, was a professional geologist who did his main work on the pre-Cambrian Stornoway Beds in Lewis. In retirement he lived in Southampton where he was an Honorary Vice-President of the Southampton Natural History Society and a member of the Borough Council. He died at the age of eighty-five, a rather eccentric, awe-inspiring but endearing character who was the epitome of courtesy.

Of the many botanists who have explored the Western Isles I select just two for mention. The Rev John Lightfoot who was Pennant's companion must have been one of the earliest plant lovers to wander amongst the rich alpine treasures in the mountains of Skye and Rhum. He it was who in 1772 discovered the mossy cyphel *Cherleria sedoides* growing on the mountain of Barkeval on Rhum, the first record for the British Isles and amongst many other plants located moonwort *Botrychium lunaria* and frog orchid *Coenoglossum viride* on Skye. On this mammoth expedition he gained valuable material for his book *Flora Scotica* published in 1778.

The second man is a modern who botanised throughout the islands up to the middle of the present century. His approach was as different from that of Lightfoot as can be imagined, indeed to classify him merely as a botanist is to diminish his great stature. It is only because of his notable contribution in this field that for the sake of convenience he has been placed in this section. John William Heslop-Harrison was born in the village of Birtley in the county of Durham in 1881. He lived most of his life in that village and died there in 1967. But like Pennant before him there was nothing parochial in his make-up. An early interest in natural history was instilled and fostered by close relatives and by a neighbour and he maintained this broad approach to nature all his life. After a period as a school teacher during which he carried out field studies in the neighbouring county of Yorkshire he was appointed Professor of Botany at Durham University a post which he held for many years. He was far from being a narrow specialist and his own particular concern was in biogeography, a subject which enabled him to maintain the comprehensive viewpoint. His association with the Hebrides began in 1932 when he led a biological expedition to South Rona, followed the next year by another to Raasay. By this time the Hebrides had claimed another devoted 'victim' and he was fired with an enthusiasm not only to discover the plants and invertebrate life but also to study the complicated and confused picture of their origin. He worked as the leader of a team of scientists whose members varied over the years but who made valuable contributions in their own right. He was that rare combination of field naturalist and laboratory experimenter and must be accounted a biogeographer of the first rank. He contributed a very large number of scientific papers on Hebridean entomology and botany to a variety of journals and it is to be regretted that he never wrote a book on this subject.

It was not until the nineteenth century that ornithologists began to discover the islands' abundant birdlife. Neil Mackenzie, Church of Scotland minister on St Kilda for fourteen years from 1829 onwards, made detailed records of its birds and it was this island group together with the other more remote islands, which seemed to attract the attention of the early birdwatchers. James Wilson was one such who, together with Sir Thomas Lauder, Secretary of the Board of Fisheries, visited St Kilda in 1841. The following year he published a book *Voyage round the Coasts of Scotland*. The famous Kearton brothers visited St Kilda in 1896 on the tourist steamer from Glasgow. Sons of a Yorkshire farmer they were pioneer bird photographers. Richard concentrated his activity on natural history writing whilst his brother Cherry devoted his time to photography; they were a notable partnership. Cherry photographed a fulmar in close-up on St Kilda; probably the first man to do so.

Dr William Eagle Clark, who was born in 1853, became Natural History Keeper at the Royal Scottish Museum, Edinburgh. He specialised in bird migration studies and although his work was concentrated on Fair Isle he did not neglect the Hebrides. He spent five weeks on St Kilda in the autumn of 1910 and 1911 and must be one of very few naturalists who have spent more than a day or so on the Flannans, for he stayed on Eilean Mor for a fortnight in 1904. He was in regular correspondence with the lighthouse keepers on the remote Hebridean outliers who supplied him with information on the migrant birds they observed.

The two well known Scottish women ornithologists Evelyn V. Baxter and Leonora J. Rintoul paid visits, sometimes separately but chiefly together, on a number of occasions over a period of about forty years from 1910 onwards casting their observant eyes about them and making careful records of the birdlife seen. Islands they explored included Rhum and Skye in

1910, Lewis in 1911 and 1932, Coll in 1929, the Outer Isles in 1932, North Uist in 1934, Iona and Mull in 1948. Mary, Duchess of Bedford, was a nature lover with a great interest in birdlife who delighted in cruising amongst the more remote Hebridean islands in her motor yacht *Sapphire*. She was an intrepid woman and scrambled ashore over slippery rocks on isolated stacks at a time when such activity was considered distinctly unladylike. Her expeditions within the region included landings on North Rona in 1907 and 1910. She was an early aeroplane pilot and lost her life when flying solo over flooded East Anglian fenland in March 1937.

James Fisher must surely be accounted the doyen of those recent ornithologists who were Hebridophiles. His first love apart from ornithology was exploring islands, the more remote the better, and in the Hebrides he could combine these two recreations to perfection. St Kilda and Rockall were his two especial concerns and it must have been one of the great thrills of his life when he was landed on Rockall in September 1955. He wrote numerous articles and books and amongst the latter were *The Fulmar* in 1952 and *Rockall* in 1956, both books containing a massive accumulation of facts. He died tragically at the age of fifty-eight as the result of a car accident in London in September 1970 when at the zenith of his achievements.

The study of the invertebrate life of the isles really only got under way during the present century when a few experts began their investigations and this is being extended by entomologists who are compiling faunal lists on the National Nature Reserves. The foregoing list is a very selective one concentrating on the more notable naturalists of the many who found their way across the Minch.

CHAPTER TWO

Geology

Island formation—Stratigraphy—Glaciation—
Geology and wildlife

ISLAND FORMATION

THE GEOLOGICAL HISTORY OF the Hebrides spans well over 2,000 million years although for much of this time they were not islands but part of a large land mass which itself varied enormously in extent and was at intervals either in whole or in part submerged beneath the waves of ancient seas.

Before we trace the succession of rocks, however, let us look briefly at the relatively recent development of the region into islands. It is quite impossible to be categoric about details of their formation and much must remain a matter of conjecture. The scanty evidence in the field lies in the raised beaches, the offshore peat and the isthmuses known as 'tarberts'. The Outer Hebrides are separated from the mainland by the channel called the Minch. There is considerable difference of opinion both as to the date and manner of its construction. It is sometimes referred to as a rift valley. This is a block of land which has subsided between two faults, but in this technical sense the Minch is probably not a rift valley since although a fault is known to exist in the western part parallel to the eastern coast of Lewis, no such fault has been found on the mainland side. It may well have originated in one of those mammoth earth movements which geologists term 'tectonic'. Various dates have been suggested from the Secondary era to the beginning of the Pliocene period in the Tertiary era, only ten million years ago.

If the initial step in the formation of the Hebrides was land subsidence it is probable that this was followed by the development of an extensive river system on the area which is now the Minch with a main river whose course flowed close to the eastern shore of Harris and Lewis along the line of the fault mentioned above. Faults are always particularly susceptible to erosion and over the centuries the river would have carved out a deep channel which much later would have been enlarged still more by the forces of marine erosion when the sea flooded in. There was another factor, too. When the glaciers slid off the Scottish mainland they gouged out a number of great basins in the Minch. The deepest of these basins is in the Inner Sound of Raasay off the north-east coast of the island where the depth reaches 1,500ft (457m) but there are others exceeding 1,000ft (305m) at various places, for example, in the Sound of Jura and the Cuillin Sound in the Inner Hebrides and off the shores of Barra and Harris in the Outer Isles. So fluviatile, marine and glacial erosion in addition to subsidence have all played their part in the origin of these western islands.

So far in this chapter the implicit assumption is that there was one marine transgression which separated the Hebrides from the mainland. But it is at least possible that there was more than one invasion of the sea. Certainly it is likely that the Outer Isles were separated well before the Inner. With a map in front of one it takes no great feat of imagination to visualise Mull and Skye as part of the mainland and Islay and Jura as forming a companion peninsula to that of Kintyre. The isolated St Kildan group may have formed part of one land mass with the Outer Hebrides in relatively recent times. After the cutting off of St Kilda the Outer Isles remained one, the aptly-named Long Island, until the post-glacial period when the sea level rose and drowned some of the ancient river valleys. The raised beaches which are so numerous in many of the islands of the Inner Hebrides indicate changes in level of both land and sea from glacial times onward. Those which occur on the western coast of Jura and the north-east cliffs of Islay are regarded as being the finest raised beaches in Europe. Their absence from the Outer Hebrides may indicate that the land there has either not risen since the Ice Age or has risen less than the sea.

It must be realised that the pattern of islands is the consequence of a continuous process for the land rose as well as the sea. An examination of the physical map reveals narrow necks of low-lying land at a number of places, for example, in Jura, Harris, Eriskay and Barra, where only a small change in the relative levels of land and sea would produce new islands. Erosion is another factor which is capable of producing islands as well as stacks and it is considered that the eastern peninsula of Pabbay will eventually become another island if the present erosion of the neck continues. Although the fragmentation of the land is the most conspicuous feature at the present day the formation of the Hebrides was not entirely a one-way operation. Islands have been joined as well as separated and there is some evidence that Islay and Colonsay in the geologically recent past were split into several islands.

STRATIGRAPHY

The oldest part of the entire group is the central area of the Outer Hebrides consisting of the northern part of South Uist, Benbecula and North Uist where the rocks of Lewisian Gneiss exceed 2,200 million years. Almost the whole of the Outer Isles with their northern outliers, Tiree, Coll, part of the Sleat peninsula on Skye, Rona, the northern tip of Raasay, the western half of Iona and the southern half of the Rhinns of Islay consist of rocks of this formation. These gneissose rocks are metamorphic, that is, they have been changed from their original nature by the intense pressures of earth movements which in this part of the country have been of a regional rather than localised character. Most of these were in the first instance igneous rocks from a molten magma below the surface which in their present state are described as ortho-gneisses. In a few areas in Harris and some of the Inner Hebrides the gneisses were formed from sedimentary material and these are called para-gneisses. Both types indicate a

high degree of metamorphism. The banding which is characteristic of schists is still present but the bands lack the fissile nature
of the schistose layers. A striking feature of the gneiss in the
Outer Isles is the zone of shattered rocks, known to geologists as
the flinty crush, which stretches from the outlier of Sula Sgeir
southwards along the eastern coast for 160 miles (257km) from
the Butt of Lewis to Barra where it passes to the western side
and continues to Sandray. This is the site of a thrust plane where
another mass of gneiss moved north-westwards from the area of
the Minch crushing the underlying rocks. The earliest intrusions
of igneous rock occur during the Lewisian period; these include
the granite masses of Harris and Lewis and in the former area the
coarse crystalline rocks known as pegmatites which were formed
during a late stage in the crystallisation of the magma. Some of
these latter rocks are radioactive and it is not therefore advisable
for specimens to be carried in the pockets of one's clothes.

The desert sands of the Torridonian strata were laid down
some 600 million years ago on the surface of the gneiss. Although they still cover a large area of the western mainland only
a relatively small proportion remains in the Western Isles. In
Lewis, beds of conglomerate in the district of Stornoway are
generally accepted as being of this period although they have
been the subject of some controversy. In the Inner Hebrides
Torridonian strata occupy parts of south-east Skye, Raasay,
Rhum, Scalpay, Iona and the Rhinns of Islay and virtually the
whole of Colonsay and Oronsay. Apart from sandstone and
conglomerate there are shales, flagstones and greywackes, the
last named being rocks containing a variety of minerals cemented
together with silica.

The remaining rocks of the pre-Cambrian era are those of the
Moine and Dalradian series. The former is poorly represented in
relatively small areas of Mull and the south-west corner of the
Sleat peninsula on Skye. The Dalradian rocks are found, as
might be expected from their distribution on the mainland, only
in the southern part of the Inner Hebrides from Lismore south to
Islay. They occupy only part, albeit the largest part, of the

latter island but comprise virtually the whole of the remaining
dozen or so islands with the exception of Colonsay and Oronsay
mentioned above. Like the Moine series these too are mainly
metamorphic. The large island of Jura and the small isle of
Lunga, much of Islay, Scarba and the Isles of the Sea consist of
quartzite. This has produced massive screes on the Paps of Jura,
very striking in appearance but providing an exhausting scramble
for the hill climber. The scenery of this formation is wild moorland with ling the principal constituent. The island of Seil together with its neighbours are sometimes called the Slate Islands
because of the Dalradian slates which were once extensively
quarried there. Phyllites, which represent a stage of metamorphism in the transition from slates to schists, occupy the
central and south-eastern parts of Islay. The low fertile island of
Lismore in the Firth of Lorne consists of Dalradian limestone and
there are extensive deposits on Islay where it is quarried. In
north-east Islay there are veins in the limestone containing
galena (lead ore) and other minerals and lead was mined from
the Middle Ages to the nineteenth century. The uneven ground
in the Loch Finlaggan area resembles the 'gruffy' ground of the
old lead mines on the Mendips in south-west England.

The history of the pre-Cambrian, the most ancient of geological eras, is as shrouded in the mists of obscurity as the Hebrides are themselves when sea fogs descend. With the advent
500 million years ago of the Cambrian period of the succeeding
Palaeozoic era, the mist lifts temporarily to reveal a vast ocean
covering the whole of the British Isles including the Hebrides
with the shoreline of a northern land mass well to the north of
the Butt of Lewis. Although the Hebrides lay under this and the
succeeding Ordovician sea for about 150 million years the only
evidence of their sediments existing in the region today are the
Cambrian deposits covering a relatively small area of Skye and a
few glacier-borne erratics of this age on the island of North
Rona. There followed during Silurian times the gigantic Caledonian earth movements and in this period the whole of the
Hebrides and the Highlands of Scotland formed one land mass.

One of these movements resulted in the initial formation of the Great Glen and the southward extension of this appears as the Loch Gruinart Fault in Islay. Another such movement was the Moine Thrust which stretches for many miles along the Scottish mainland and in the Hebrides divides the Lewisian and Torridonian strata in Skye. Farther south it is believed to pass under the channel separating Iona from Mull and beyond this may emerge as the Loch Skerrols Thrust on Islay.

In the next period Old Red Sandstone sediments were laid down in Scotland in marine basins. The southern outlet of the Orcadie Basin engulfed the land comprising the more southerly of the Inner Hebrides and some volcanic activity also occurred at this time. Very few rocks of this age can be seen in the Hebrides today. They are, however, exposed in the core of an anticline in south-east Mull. Dykes of Lower Old Red Sandstone were intruded on Scarba and laval flows attributed to this period are found on Mull. Jura and Colonsay have scattered ice-borne rocks conveyed from some unknown source within the basin.

During the whole of the Carboniferous period which followed and which lasted for sixty million years the Hebrides were part of a Scandinavian land mass and there are no deposits of this age within the region. At the end of this period came the second series of major earth movements which are known either as Armorican or Hercynian. In the Hebrides faults on Mull may be assigned to this time. For perhaps another forty million years the region remained above sea level and then the Inner Hebrides were submerged by the late Triassic shallow lagoons. New Red Sandstones of this age are found on the little island of Inch Kenneth off the west coast of Mull, in northern Rhum and in small deposits on Mull, Raasay and Skye. New Red Sandstone is an omnibus term covering, in addition to sandstone, marl, breccia and conglomerates which contain pebbles of the old Palaezoic rocks.

These brackish lakes were flooded by the Rhaetic sea. Beds of this period, identified by their fossil content, are exposed at Gribun in western Mull and may also exist at another locality in

Skye. Jurassic sediments are very scarce in Scotland generally and
the most extensive exposures are in the Inner Hebrides. The Lias
or Lower Jurassic deposits are located in Raasay, eastern Skye,
several areas in the southern half of Mull and in the Outer
Hebrides on the Shiant Isles in the middle of the Minch. The
characteristic fossils, including ammonites, are abundant in some
localities. The rock types are varied and include ironstone,
shales, sandstones and limestones. In the Shiants the Liassic
shales lie under the igneous sill of which the islands principally
consist. Later Jurassic formations occur in the same three Inner
Hebridean islands and also in Muck, Eigg and Scalpay. The
region is the type locality for the fossil *Liostrea hebridica* which is
not, however, restricted to this area. The instability of Jurassic
sediments is well known and landslips have taken place at Gribun
in Mull and at the Storr and Quiraing in north-east Skye where
the fragmentation and subsequent erosion of the overlying
basaltic lavas have produced a number of bizarre pillars and pin-
nacles of rock. It ought perhaps to be mentioned in passing that
the name 'Jurassic' does not derive from the Hebridean island of
Jura but from the Jura mountains in eastern France.

Beds of the succeeding Cretaceous rocks are sparse indeed.
Thin layers of greensand and chalk of the Upper Cretaceous are
found in south-east Mull and small areas of rocks of this period
are found elsewhere, sandstones and marl in northern Eigg and
other sediments in Raasay and Skye. The small amount of chalk
present has been subject to alteration and does not resemble the
chalk of English downland.

The extent of the Cretaceous sea in Scotland is in doubt but
what is not in question is that with the ending of the Cretaceous
period some sixty-five million years ago the Hebridean region
rose from the sea and some ten to twenty million years later
became the scene of volcanic activity on a gigantic scale. This
centred on four areas, Mull, Skye, Rhum and St Kilda and in
some places has resulted in a very complicated geological pattern.
It will be sufficient here to express it in the simplest possible
terms. From the neck of the volcanoes issued a succession of im-

Plate 5 (above) Corncrake at Houghgarry, North Uist
Plate 6 (below) Valtos Glen, Lewis, a glacial overflow channel

Plate 7 (above) Grass–of–Parnassus, Arnabost, Coll
Plate 8 (below) Red grouse on Islay moorland

mense laval flows which swept over a large area much of which is under the sea today but including parts of Mull, Muck, Eigg, Canna, Skye and Raasay. The dark basaltic lavas are up to 6,000ft (1,829m) thick in places and cover over 700 square miles (1,813sq km) of the Inner Hebrides. Several interesting features arise from these volcanic deposits. In Mull and also in north-west Skye the layers of basalt are interspersed with sediments which contain fossil leaf impressions and these enabled the Tertiary age of the igneous rocks to be established long before the modern methods of rock dating were available. The most spectacular of the fossils is a 40ft (12·2m) tree embedded in the cliff on the peninsula north of Loch Scridain. Another attribute relates to the typical terraced landform of the lava country which again is clearly illustrated in Mull as well as other islands. A third is the hexagonal columns into which the cooling basalt is sometimes formed and for which the island of Staffa is famous. Almost as notable a topographic feature is the prominent landmark of the Scuir of Eigg. Made of pitchstone, which is a glassy volcanic rock, its origin has long been a matter of controversy. Since this rock is known from islets elsewhere and since it contains fragments of fossilised wood it has been suggested that it originated as laval flows following the course of an ancient river. The columns of the dolerite sill in the Shiants are exceptionally fine, some of them being over 300ft (91m) high and 9ft (2·7m) in diameter.

Both acid and basic intrusive magmas were formed below the surface and subsequently exposed by erosion. All the four areas have both types. The granite of the Red Hills and the gabbro of the Cuillins are examples in Skye; the light-coloured granitic type rock in the eastern part of Hirta and the gabbros and dolerites of the western part are St Kilda's contribution; Rhum has granite in the west and a variety of ultra-basic rocks in the south and Mull has granitic rocks and gabbro. One of the ultrabasic rock types on Rhum has been named allivalite after the mountain of that name and alternating bands of this rock which is a pale form of gabbro are conspicuous on Allival and Askival.

D

The banding is due to the varying mineral content of the layers. Another distinctively Scottish rock type is rockallite, a dark variety of the granite of which Rockall is composed. The presence of granite on this extremely isolated stack presumably indicates the existence of another centre of volcanic activity in the neighbourhood of the Rockall Bank.

In addition to these large masses of igneous rock there are numerous dykes where magma has forced its way up through fissures and joints. These dykes are found not only in many of the Inner Isles but also in some of the Outer Hebrides and they follow a definite north-west trend. Those on Islay and Jura are not easily correlated with the Mull complex and may relate to an unlocated volcanic centre now submerged by the Sound of Jura. Mull, like Ardnamurchan on the mainland, has roughly circular ring dykes and basaltic cone-sheets which are normally very narrow dykes semi-circular in outline where they outcrop on the surface but inclining inwards under the ground thus forming the approximate shape of a cone. Another intrusive rock structure is the sill which unlike a dyke is a horizontal flow of magma between, rather than across, rock strata. Many sills exist in Mull and Skye. An exceptionally large dolerite sill occurs in the north-east part of the latter island. By late Tertiary times extensive erosion had made great inroads into the volcanic rocks and Alpine earth movements had effected much folding of the underlying strata.

GLACIATION

With the ending of the Tertiary era came the Ice Age with its four major glaciations. Glaciers existed on the mountains of Mull and Skye and in the hills of Harris in the Outer Hebrides and in addition the islands were affected by the west-flowing glaciers of the Scottish mainland; for example, ice from Rannoch Moor moved south-westwards across Jura and Islay and from the mountains of western Inverness-shire and Wester Ross across to Sky and the Outer Hebrides. Till or boulder clay is well distributed in the Inner Hebrides and in the western and northern parts

of Lewis. In the last named area they contain molluscan shells of
varying climatic conditions ranging from the bivalve *Astarte
semisulcata* and the gastropod *Trophonopsis clathratus* which today
have an Arctic distribution to a gastropod of warm water *Sipho
jeffreysianus*. The rounded hummocks of boulder clay known as
drumlins are a feature of the island of Baleshare and the adjoining
coast on North Uist. Occasionally quite large boulders, termed
erratics, are transported by the ice over considerable distances.
The well known Ringing Stone of Tiree is an erratic from Rhum
and indicates a south-west movement of the ice; Jura and
Colonsay have erratics from Argyllshire. Few occur in the Outer
Hebrides but boulders of Cambrian and Torridonian age have
been identified on North Rona and the Flannans have a number
of erratics.

Erosion is the other major consequence of glaciation. Apart
from the marine basins which were mentioned earlier some of
the lochs are the result of moving glaciers. Loch Coruisk in Skye
is a splendid example. Scratches made by ice on the rocks, called
glacial striae, are abundant both in the Inner and Outer Isles and
the mainly north-west orientation of these marks indicate the
direction of the ice-sheet movements. Valtos Glen in western
Lewis is a striking natural phenomenon which was probably a
glacial meltwater valley. It would appear that the westward
movement of the glaciers stopped short of St Kilda although
small local glaciers formed.

GEOLOGY AND WILDLIFE

The mineral content of the rocks greatly influences the nature
and extent of the vegetation. The rock structure, for example,
whether permeable or impermeable, easily broken down into
cultivable soil or highly resistant, is a basic determinant of the
habitat. The non-acid rocks, that is, the Dalradian, Cambrian
and Jurassic limestones and the basaltic lava flows have a richer
flora than the acid rocks which have a high silica content. The
rich green of those pastures on Islay which are on Dalradian

limestone stand out from the other rock types of the series and these fields have certain lime-loving orchids in their plant communities. The calcium content of the shell-sand beaches on western coasts has enriched the machair flora after the prevailing westerlies have blown the shell-sand over the dunes. A further outcome of this has been that the increased alkalinity of the machair lochs supports more aquatic plant species than the acid lochs of the moors. The basalts with their low silica content carry numerous wild flowers, in some instances, notably in north-east Skye, very rare species.

The marine erosion, which in many of the islands has chiselled out caves along lines of fracture or along igneous dykes where these are softer than the surrounding country rock, has provided nest sites for choughs on Islay and for rock doves throughout the islands. Red deer on Jura are reported to make use of the island's many west coast caves for shelter in inclement conditions. In the main, however, the effects of geology on wildlife are of an indirect character and the distribution of animals is more immediately influenced by the physical geography.

CHAPTER THREE

The coastline

Cliffs—Rocky shores—Outliers, stacks and skerries—
Coastal waters

CLIFFS

THE HEBRIDES POSSESS A splendid array of sea cliffs some of which
are of magnificent proportions surpassing even the finest sections of the mainland coast. They are so extensive that it is not
possible to list them and they exhibit a considerable variety of
rock types. They range from the most ancient of all, the tremendous cliffs of Lewisian Gneiss in the Outer Isles, through
Dalradian metamorphic rocks in the more southerly of the Inner
Hebrides, Torridonian Sandstone on Islay, Colonsay and Rhum,
sections of Mesozoic sediments in several places including Mull,
Skye and Raasay, Tertiary basaltic lavas in a number of islands
including Mull where they form the great cliffs of Ardmeanach
in the south-west, to the geologically recent, a cliff of glacial
boulder clay at Traigh Chunil in north-west Lewis. The most
spectacular of all the Hebridean cliffs is the mighty Conachair on
St Kilda, at 1,397ft (425m) the highest sea cliff in the British Isles.
The next highest cliff in the Hebrides is Biulacraig on Mingulay
with an impressive vertical face of 700ft (213m) to the Atlantic.

Sea cliffs provide a variety of conditions from extreme exposure to relative shelter, from perennially wet ledges to dry
thin soils, in which plants can establish a foothold. An outstanding feature applicable to this and similar large groups of islands
is that the cliffs are orientated to all points of the compass.

Despite the miscellany of rock type its principal effect on plant life lies chiefly in the acid or alkaline character of the rock. The predominant factor is the exposure both to salt spray and frequent gale-force winds. A certain specialised plant community, whose members have developed adaptations enabling them to live in these exacting conditions, is common on cliffs throughout Britain although in the Hebrides there is considerable variety in distribution and a plant which is common enough on one island may be scarce or even absent on the next a few miles away. As conditions in saltmarshes are very similar to the conditions on the cliffs some species are common to both situations. Thrift or sea pink *Armeria maritima*, rose-root *Sedum rosea*, English stonecrop *S. anglicum*, sea plantain *Plantago maritima*, buck's-horn plantain *P. coronopus*, common scurvy-grass *Cochlearia officinalis* and sea campion *Silene maritima* are amongst the most frequently encountered species. The succulent leaves of the stonecrop and rose-root are their method of adjusting to the xerophytic conditions caused by the drying winds. The narrow leaves of thrift and buck's-horn plantain are their way of combating drought whilst the sea plantain employs both methods, having leaves which are narrow and fleshy. Another plant with succulent leaves is samphire *Crithmum maritimum* which in the main grows in south-west England but occurs also in south-west Scotland; it has been recorded from Islay and reaches its most northerly British station on the cliffs of Uig in western Lewis. The maritime sub-species of the scentless mayweed *Tripleurospermum maritimum* is widespread from Islay in the south to Lewis in the north. The cliffs of the Garvellachs have societies of crow garlic *Allium vineale* which is a rare flower in Scotland. Curled dock *Rumex crispus*, rock spurrey *Spergularia rupicola*, early purple orchid *Orchis mascula* and golden rod *Solidago virgaurea* are occasionals in the sea cliff community.

Moist cliff ledges may have the saltmarsh rush *Juncus gerardii*, angelica *Angelica sylvestris*, golden saxifrage *Chrysoplenium oppositifolium* and tutsan *Hypericum androsaemum* which is recorded as occasional in the Small Isles but rare on Coll and Tiree. The royal fern *Osmunda regalis* grows on moist ledges and gullies on a number of islands including Islay, Jura and Rhum. Some of the cliff dwellers have a preference for basic rocks although they are not necessarily confined to them, kidney vetch *Anthyllis vulneraria*, mountain avens *Dryas octopetala*, carline thistle *Carlina vulgaris*, and sea and green spleenworts *Asplenium marinum* and *A. viride*. Of this list the sea spleenwort is probably the most widespread, the others being local or rare.

In addition to the foregoing the cliffs have a number of specialities which in Britain have a principally Scottish distribution. The globe flower *Trollius europaeus* although not restricted to Scotland is essentially a northern plant of mountainous areas which grows here and there on moist coastal ledges. The specific name of one of the umbellifers reveals its distinctively Scottish association; this is lovage *Ligusticum scoticum* a typical plant of Hebridean cliffs although its numerical status varies from island to island; for example, it is recorded as abundant on Rhum and most of the other Small Isles, only fairly common on Coll and scarce or absent on Tiree, Gunna and Muck. The northern scurvy grass *Cochlearia scotica* is frequent on some cliffs and is reported to be the commonest scurvy grass in the Outer Hebrides. The occurrence of a moss from the Canary Islands, the Hebridean moss *Myurium hebridarum*, has already been mentioned in Chapter One. I have found the beautiful pink-studded cushions of the moss campion *Silene acaulis* in abundance on the cliffs of Mangersta in Lewis and it grows also on Canna, St Kilda, Skye, the eastern coast of Raasay and the north-west cliffs of Berneray. The early spring-flowering purple saxifrage *Saxifraga oppositifolia* drapes the rocks in the gullies on the Mull of Oa on Islay. The woolly-leaved mountain everlasting *Antennaria dioica* has been recorded growing at sea level on Muck. Mountain avens, which has already been mentioned in the list of calcophiles, grows in abundance on the calcareous cliffs of Raasay. Mountain sorrel *Oxyria digyna* is an alpine which normally grows on moist rocks high in the mountains but in the Hebrides it exists on the cliffs of Raasay and Mingulay. It is considered that at the latter station the species has survived from pre-glacial times.

There is another intriguing aspect of Hebridean cliff flora; in some places plants of woodland habitat grow on the ledges, sometimes on a quite extensive scale. Bluebells *Endymion non-scripta*, primroses *Primula vulgaris*, lesser celandine *Ranunculus ficaria*, red campion *Silene dioica* and rosebay willow herb *Chamaenerion angustifolium* are essentially woodland plants often growing in very sheltered conditions but in the Hebrides they occupy very exposed sites on the cliffs. In early summer there is a colourful spectacle on Barra where coastal hills such as Greian Head and Ben Eoligarry are carpeted with primroses and this plant can be found from Islay to as far afield as St Kilda. Another small woodland flower is the wood sorrel *Oxalis acetosella* which is common on the cliffs of Coll. Dun Chonnuill in the Garvellachs has dog's mercury *Mercurialis perennis*, that characteristic plant of hazel coppices, growing plentifully in cliff crevices. Wood false-brome *Brachypodium sylvaticum* and wood horsetail *Equisetum sylvaticum* growing with *Rosa dumalis* on cliffs behind Mingulay Bay may be indicative of a former woodland association in the opinion of Dr W. A. Clark who was a member of Professor Heslop-Harrison's team which carried out extensive field studies in the Hebrides. An uncommon tree of calcareous rocks, the rock white beam *Sorbus rupicola*, grows on the Jurassic limestone cliffs of Raasay; on this island and in the Outer Hebrides holly and ivy are found on the coastal cliffs. Aspens *Populus tremula* are frequent on the cliff ledges of Rhum and some of the Outer Isles and the eared willow *Salix aurita* is recorded from Benbecula. Honeysuckle *Lonicera periclymenum* on the Hebridean cliffs has evolved into a glossy and thick-leaved form, var *clarkii*.

Some members of the cliff top community also grow on slopes and ledges but in general it is a distinct association. Typical plants are the vernal squill *Scilla verna*, procumbent pearlwort *Sagina procumbens*, sea pearlwort *S. maritima*, sea carrot *Daucus carota*, crowberry *Empetrum nigrum* and dark-green mouse-ear chickweed *Cerastium atrovirens*. In some localities such as the Uig cliffs of Lewis and Greian Head on Barra there is a flower of calcareous pastures, the frog orchid *Coeloglossum viride* and on Mingulay the abundance of sea spray enables sea milk-wort *Glaux maritima*, a plant of the saltmarsh, to thrive. Charac-teristic grasses of cliff tops are red fescue *Festuca rubra*, sheep's fescue *F. ovina*, Yorkshire fog *Holcus lanatus*, wavy hair grass *Deschampsia flexuosa* and early hair grass *Aira praecox*.

A number of invertebrate studies have been made but much still remains to be discovered. The islands which have probably received most attention in this respect are Canna and Rhum in the Small Isles. There is a popular fallacy that the proximity of the sea with its breezes brings relief from the biting midges but in fact this unwelcome family of insects is present in abundance even on the Atlantic-facing cliffs. The cliff top sward has ground beetles prominent amongst the insect fauna and 'staph' beetles together with weevils of several genera inhabit seabirds' nests. The attractive little dew moth *Setina irrorella* occupies this specialised habitat by reason of the caterpillars' food preference for the brightly-coloured lichens which grow on coastal cliffs. The moth has black-spotted, buff-coloured forewings and its vernacular name derives from the rather fanciful resemblance to a dewdrop when the insect is at rest. This moth is recorded from Rhum, Canna and Skye and may well be present on other of the Inner Hebrides. The grey *Hadena caesia* is another very un-common moth which is specifically associated with sea cliffs due to the food plant of the caterpillar being sea campion. This insect in the British Isles is known only from Ireland, the Isle of Man, Rhum and Canna. The treble-bar *Anaitis plagiata* is one of the more common and widespread species which flies on some of the cliffs where species of St John's wort grow. The belted beauty *Nyssa zonaria* is a moth of the Hebridean dunes but it has been recorded from the southern cliffs of Canna. Several moths not normally associated with coastal cliffs have been identified on the cliffs of this island. They include the chevron *Lygris testata* of moorland and the grass rivulet *Perizoma albulata* of meadows.

Despite their compelling interest to the plant geographer and the surprises they may yet produce for the entomologist the mighty gale-swept bastions of the Hebrides hold their greatest treasures in trust for the man or woman whose eyes are enthralled by the sight of kittiwakes falling like giant snowflakes from the cliffs; whose heart misses a beat as a peregrine hurtles into the air from his cliff top vantage point and encircles the walker with a barricade of strident calls; whose hearing is stimulated by the guttural growls of the auks and the unearthly nocturnal cries of the Manx shearwaters as they drop to their cliff top burrows; whose aesthetic sensitivities are heightened by the effortless gliding of fulmars along the cliff face; whose gaze is delighted by the aerial aerobatics of choughs and whose sense of humour is titillated by a row of puffins who like many great comedians have but to take the stage to provoke laughter. When a person to whom all these sights and sounds are meaningful tires of the Hebridean cliffs he will be, in the words of Dr Samuel Johnson, 'tired of life'.

In these days when modesty is almost accounted a crime and the world echoes *ad nauseum* to the shouts of the greatest, the Hebrides can proudly join in the competitive stakes. For example, North Rona's great black-backed gull population of over 500 pairs may be the largest in Britain. St Kilda possesses the largest gannetry in the world with 45,000 pairs on Stac an Armin, Stac Lee and Boreray. On the main island of Hirta St Kilda has the largest fulmar colony in the British Isles. The next biggest is probably on those southern outposts of the Outer Isles, Mingulay and Berneray. Despite a decline of considerable magnitude St Kildan cliffs still hold a huge colony of puffins with some 250,000 pairs and there is another vast population on the Shiants. Although seabird communities are spread throughout the islands their distribution is localised as the physical conditions must be suitable with ledges required for most of the species, rock clitter and crevices for razorbills and storm petrels, burrows for puffins, shearwaters and Leach's petrels.

The speciality of Hebridean seabirds is the Leach's fork-tailed petrel. Although it cannot be reckoned a rare bird, at least in terms of numbers, this species is virtually restricted in Britain to four Hebridean localities and is one of a few resident species which probably most British birdwatchers have not seen. The reason for this elusiveness is the remoteness of its breeding haunts, its nocturnal habits at the nesting site and its pelagic sojourning outside the breeding season. These petrels nest on most of the islands and stacks of St Kilda, six of the Flannans, Sula Sgeir and North Rona which last probably has the largest population in Britain. An interesting ringing recovery was of a bird ringed originally on North Rona and retrapped there thirteen years later. The Leach's are much noisier on the wing than storm petrels and have different call notes. These differences are not easy to describe and it is advisable for a would-be Leach's hunter to familiarise himself with recordings of the two species.

Storm petrel breeding stations are more widespread occurring in a number of localities in St Kilda, the Flannans and a few of the smaller more isolated islands in the Inner and Outer Isles. Despite the wider distribution there is some evidence that on those islands where both species nest the Leach's are ousting the Stormies. Although the storm petrel nests mainly in old dry stone walls, under boulders or in crevices, it occasionally excavates a burrow in turf. The Manx shearwater is another nocturnal, burrow-nesting petrel which breeds in colonies mainly, but not always, on sea cliffs. Some colonies are located on certain coastal cliffs of a few islands including Eigg, Canna, St Kilda and probably the Treshnish Isles. To be in the midst of such a colony at midnight is an exciting experience for any lover of wildlife as the air above is filled with a medley of stirring cries and birds drop from the darkness to land at one's feet. Gliding over the crests of the waves in beautiful flight the shearwater is master of its environment but on land it is clumsy, virtually helpless and can easily be picked up. Until the last century a novel form of rent was paid by the tenants of Mingulay to the owner, MacNeil of Barra. This consisted of an annual payment of young shearwaters proportioned out according to the size of the crofts and totalling twenty barrels a year. One more petrel is a breeder in the Hebrides; this is the fulmar whose dramatic spread is one of the notable features of British ornithology in recent times. It is possible here to sketch only the bare outline and the reader desirous of a full account is referred to *The Fulmar* by James Fisher. The stronghold of this species in the British Isles has always been St Kilda and up to 1878 this island group was the only place in Britain where the birds bred, an outlier of their far northern breeding grounds. To the St Kildans the fulmar was a very important item in their diet and probably 12,000–15,000 young were taken annually. It gradually overtook the gannet in popularity as a food supply and its oil was used to light lamps. Not surprisingly, visitors to St Kilda noticed that the distinctive oily smell was pervasive in every house. In 1877 the naturalist J. A. Harvie-Brown observed a great increase in the fulmar population on St Kilda and the following year they nested for the first time on Noss and Foula in Shetland. The spread had begun although strangely enough it is probable that the Shetland occupation at least came from the Faeroes. In the Hebrides the first localities to be colonised were Sula Sgeir and North Rona in 1887 and by 1902 colonisation of the Outer Isles had begun. Breeding commenced on Skye in 1930 and rather surprisingly in view of the general southward nature of the spread, Islay had fulmar nests six years earlier. As the populations grew fulmars became more flexible in their habitat requirements and nested at quite low levels. St Kilda still has the largest number with perhaps some 40,000 pairs and it is considered that the period of expansion in the Hebrides may now have come to an end. Unlike the other three petrels, the fulmar is diurnal and on the cliffs nests in the open on ledges and slopes. It shares the unpleasant petrel habit of ejecting an odoriferous oil from its bill at intruders who venture too close. Of all the oceanic seabirds who summer in Britain the fulmar leaves the nesting area for the briefest period being absent only for a few weeks in autumn and early winter.

By size alone the gannet stands out from other British seabirds.

It is 3ft (·91m) in length and has a wing span of 6ft (1·82m). Within this region gannets nest on Sula Sgeir, St Kilda and recently in small numbers on a rock in the Flannans. The inhabitants of Ness in northern Lewis have long had a tradition of travelling in September to Sula Sgeir in order to collect young gannets, known as gugas, for food. An order made in 1955 under the Bird Protection Act, 1954, gave due recognition to this tradition by placing the Sula Sgeir gannets in the third schedule list which allows them to be killed outside the close season from 1 February to 31 August. About 3,000 gugas are taken annually; they are very much an acquired taste for a palate which is not nauseated by the flavour of cod-liver oil. Due to the remoteness of the nesting sites the ordinary holidaymaker in the region will see gannets only as black-tipped white wings plunging into the sea.

The shag is numerous and well distributed throughout the islands. Cormorants are more localised and there are gaps which are difficult to explain; they appear to be largely absent from the Inner Isles but are widespread in the Long Island and outlying islets. I have seen a close-packed collection of over fifty nests on the small skerry of Causamul off the coast of North Uist. Owing to the great scarcity of trees herons have to find other sites and occasionally nest on the cliffs as at the Loch Roag area of Lewis, the Lochboisdale cliffs on South Uist and other places.

Various birds of prey occur but one species which used to breed has disappeared not only from the region but also from Britain. Until the beginning of this century the white-tailed eagle had a number of long established cliff eyries in the islands. The sites are still known but the birds themselves are seen no longer. They last nested on Canna in 1875, on Eigg in 1877 and Rhum in 1907. All through the nineteenth century their numbers were dwindling and by 1870 most of the remaining pairs were located on the great cliffs of Skye, where it is stated that as many as forty might be seen in the air together. Within sixteen years even on this island they had become extremely scarce and what was possibly the last nesting of this magnificent bird in Scotland took place in Skye during 1916.

An important recent development on Rhum was the importation, in June 1975, of four white-tailed eagles (one male, three females) from Norway. Unfortunately, the male died but more have been obtained since and I understand there is now a total of ten birds. The intention is to accustom them gradually to freedom by the construction of artificial eyries and the phased withdrawal of assisted food supplies. It is greatly to be hoped that this venture will prove more successful than a similar experiment on Fair Isle as it would indeed be a splendid achievement if such a noble bird could be re-established as a breeding species in Britain.

The golden eagle still nests on the cliffs in certain places including the southern coasts of Islay and the western coasts of Skye. The common buzzard is plentiful enough especially in areas where the rabbit population is high; they seem particularly common on Mull and some others of the Inner Hebrides. When myxomatosis affected the rabbit population on Coll some buzzards moved south to Tiree where they then bred for the first time, but their numbers on this island have now somewhat declined. The buzzard only began colonising the Outer Isles during the present century but it is common enough there now. The status of the peregrine is very different. A heavy drop in the population took place in the early 1960s and although a BTO census in 1971 showed some improvement in inland areas of the Scottish mainland this has not been the case with the Hebridean peregrines at their coastal eyries. The report by D. A. Ratcliffe suggests that the implication of this state of affairs is that coastal peregrines which feed on seabirds are exposed to contamination by persistent toxic chemicals. This species is noted for the perseverance with which it clings to long established eyries and it is at least good to know that there are still peregrines in the Hebrides. The hovering outline of the kestrel is not an uncommon sight above the coastal cliffs of some of the Inner Isles but they are scarce in the Outer Hebrides.

Four species of gulls, great black-backed, lesser black-backed, herring and kittiwakes, nest, often in large colonies, on cliff tops, ledges and screes. Of these the herring gull is the most wide-spread and numerous although the kittiwake distribution is more concentrated, with immense numbers in some colonies. Many thousands of the latter species nest on such islands as Berneray and Mingulay and they are reported to be the commonest birds on North Rona.

The auks are another group of colonial-nesting seabirds which breed in vast numbers in the region, particularly on some of the more remote cliff-bound islands such as the Shiants, the Flannans, St Kilda, Mingulay and Berneray. Razorbills are generally less common than their relatives and associates the common guillemots; occasionally, however, in some localities they outnumber or even replace guillemots. The great auk or garefowl, now unhappily extinct, belonged to the same genus as the razorbill. Bones of the great auk have been discovered in a prehistoric midden on Oronsay but this was a bird of north Atlantic waters and within the region historic records came only from St Kilda. More than any of its relatives it had evolved into a form ideally suited for a life on the ocean but which was far from satisfactory on the land to which it came only for the short breeding period in the sub-arctic. It could not fly but its short wings and strong muscles were very effective under water. The bird's helplessness on land was its undoing and many were killed for food. It seems certain that it once nested regularly on St Kilda and Martin Martin writing in 1698 strongly implies this. In the following century the great auk's visits to this island group became irregular and by the early nineteenth century the bird was an extremely rare visitor. One was certainly present in 1821 and it is recorded that the last one in Britain was killed on Stac an Armin in 1840 although doubt has been cast on the authenticity of this record. By 1844 there were none left in the world. The northern race of the common guillemot breeds in vast aggregations in a number of colonies throughout the Hebrides especially on cliff ledges on the Outer Isles and the far outliers. The black guillemot is well distributed throughout the region but not of course in the great numbers of its larger relative. Of all the auks, puffins have suffered the greatest decline in numbers the reasons for which are not fully known. Certainly they are subject to severe predation by great black-backed gulls but since they presumably always have been this cannot be the cause. Marine pollution is a much more likely reason but it is not clear why this should have affected the puffin more than the other auks. There seems to have been a long term decline in the population; as recently as the 1950s St Kilda had an estimated three million pairs but the numbers have dwindled to about a quarter of a million pairs which is a decline of the order of ninety per cent in twenty years. The Shiants are another puffin stronghold but here again there has been a dramatic drop in numbers with an estimated twenty per cent fall in the year 1970/1. There is, however, an inexplicable but gratifying contrary trend in one or two localities and within the region puffins are on the increase in the Treshnish Isles.

A favourite nesting haunt of the rock dove is caves and these birds are fairly common and widespread in the Western Isles breeding in the caves of Islay, Jura, Mull, at Ceann a' Mhara in the south of Tiree, Eigg, Skye and throughout the Outer Hebrides up to the Butt of Lewis. On many islands it is not possible to walk very far along a cliff top without seeing the characteristic flight of a dove whose greyish white rump betokens the rock dove.

Four members of the crow family are cliff dwellers. The sizable nest of the raven is constructed quite early in the year on a cliff ledge, usually with an overhang, on the main Hebridean islands. They are less gregarious than some members of the family but they are sometimes seen in flocks and I have seen numbers at dusk flighting out to sea from North Uist to roost on an outlying skerry. Ravens display a wonderful mastery of the air and I recall watching some splendid acrobatics from a raven over Kerrera. Hooded crows are plentiful throughout the islands and in the region frequently nest on sea cliffs. Jackdaws were very scarce in the Inner Hebrides except in Cara, Gigha and Islay and were non-existent in the Outer Isles but this century has shown a considerable increase in their numbers. Eigg, for example, experienced a sixteenfold increase in just over thirty years and jackdaws are now fairly common if somewhat localised in the Inner Hebrides. They have now reached the Long Island where occasionally birds of the Scandinavian race are seen; a straggler of this race was reported from North Rona in June, 1972. The fourth member of the crow family in the region is a notable celebrity, a resident whose only breeding haunts in the whole of Scotland are on Islay. The chough is a handsome bird with its red curved bill and red feet and like the raven is in its element when the winds blow strong above the cliffs. It was once much more widespread than it is now but after only holding its own for some time in its last Hebridean strongholds it appears to be slowly increasing, although birds sometimes fall victim to rabbit-traps in winter.

Feral goats in various shades of brown, black and white roam a number of the precipitous cliffs. The long-established herd on the little island of Cara south of Gigha is mainly white. Islay has several herds in well scattered areas including the offshore island of Texa but that on the Oa peninsula is by far the largest; Jura possesses two herds, one in the south-east and the other in the north and Mull has several groups scattered across the southern part of the island. Other islands possessing goats include Oronsay, Colonsay, Shuna, and Little Colonsay but small herds often seem unable to maintain themselves and tend to die out. Those who require more detailed information are referred to *The Wild Goats of Great Britain and Ireland* by G. Kenneth Whitehead.

St Kilda is justly famous for its stock of primitive Soay sheep. For many centuries a flock probably in the region of 200 sheep have lived on Soay, a name which is almost certainly derived from the Norse and means 'Isle of sheep'. They bear a strong resemblance to Neolithic sheep which were brought into the British Isles about 7,000 years ago. No one knows when they were first introduced to St Kilda. They could have been brought by Bronze Age peoples but no archaeological evidence of a settlement of this age has yet been found. Alternatively they

E

might have been introduced by Vikings although it seems likely that they named Soay because the sheep were already there. After the evacuation of the island 107 of the sheep were transferred from Soay to Hirta in 1932. Although the numbers on Hirta have fluctuated considerably the flock had built up to a total of 1783 in 1971, in large measure owing to the richness of the pasture which in turn is due to the abundance of birds. The sheep are small and narrow bodied with two main colour types of dark and light. As well as most of the rams about fifty per cent of the ewes bear horns. In addition to the Soay sheep of Soay and Hirta, St Kilda has a large semi-feral flock of blackface sheep which lives on Boreray.

Having looked at the potential of these Hebridean cliffs let us now explore an actual cliff to see how it measures up in reality. The field below Lower Killeyan Farm on the Oa peninsula of Islay slopes down to the sea. It is late March and a blustery day. Four branches projecting above the rocks in front attract the eyes for they seem to be moving rather than just swaying in the wind. Binoculars establish that they are the horns of two wild goats, one black, the other a duo-toned black and white. They disappear below the cliff edge and by the time the walkers arrive at the spot they are a quarter of a mile away. From the short turf a hare springs up to be pursued by the farmhouse collie in an exuberant but quite futile chase.

The attractive coastline is here dotted with islets and on the nearest one a hoodie lands on the highest spot from which vantage point his crafty eyes and pivoting neck can scan a wide area. Below the surface of the water at the base of the cliff float huge masses of tangleweed from which individual strands are continually rising clear of the water like the periscopes of some inquisitive marine creatures from the world of science fiction. Farther out a black guillemot is swimming and round the island glide a succession of fulmars.

The cliffs are dark-coloured slaty rocks of the ancient Dalradian series and are indented with deep gullies whose ledges bear a varied vegetation. A vivid splash of colour on a distant ledge immediately draws attention to itself for glowing carmine flowers are almost unthinkable so early in the year. Most probably it is a piece of abandoned plastic but no, a nearer approach reveals that it is indeed a plant. This can only be the purple saxifrage which is not very appositely named since it is more red than purple. Closer inspection of the ledges shows many primroses and celandines amongst a wealth of other vegetation.

A little farther eastwards a gaggle of white-fronts arrow up into the winds which shortly will carry them to Greenland for the summer. On the numerous sheep droppings the furry yellow dung flies are already swarming. The moorland vegetation of ling and woodrush now sere and shrivelled at the end of the winter rolls up to the cliff edge. That ubiquitous bird of the moor the meadow pipit rises with the inevitable call, flat and uninspired, with which it registers mild complaint. A hundred yards deeper into the moor a red grouse whirrs away with its emotive cackle as if to demonstrate how an alarm note should really sound. On a sward which slopes steeply to the Atlantic, more goats are grazing. They are not unduly disturbed but keep a watchful eye on this intrusion and when in their judgement the watcher has come near enough they are away bounding seawards like lemmings intent on suicide; but their feet are amazingly sure and they are soon safely out of sight. The rocks have changed their character and a high promontory of conglomerate projects on to the beach below. An offshore rock is dotted white with kittiwakes settling in for another breeding season. Then suddenly but not unexpectedly, the hoped-for encounter happens. Two birds appear in the air above, flying fast in the boisterous airstream yet with nonchalant abandon for in the wild winds of March they are in their element. Their cries and the flash of red from their bills as they speed past reveal them as choughs, the highlight of the walk. The pair swing round and disappear into a cave. It is time for the satisfied observer also to leave the scene.

ROCKY SHORES

Although the flowering plants of low-lying rocky shores are in the main found also at higher levels on the cliffs the two habitats are sufficiently distinct in other ways to justify separate accounts. Green seaweeds such as *Ulva lactuca, Enteromorpha* spp and the little tufted *Cladophora rupestris* are plentiful. The common brown seaweeds between the tides follow the zonation which is general in Britain. Channel wrack *Pelvetia canaliculata* occupies the highest level where it takes on a typical dark dried-out appearance hanging in clusters like much-decayed fruit; the flat wrack *Fucus spiralis* grows immediately beneath and this is rather misleadingly named being less flat in general appearance for example than the saw-like fronds of the serrated wrack *F. serratus* which is found low on the mid-shore; between them is a zone where in sheltered conditions grows the knotted wrack *Ascophyllum nodosum* or on exposed coasts bladder wrack *Fucus vesiculosus*. At first one might think that the Hebrides would not provide a suitable terrain for knotted wrack but there are many relatively sheltered areas in sea lochs such as West Loch Tarbet on Jura, channels between islands such as the Sound of Islay and bays as on South Rona where this species grows plentifully; fronds up to 15ft (4·57m) have been recorded from the Outer Hebrides. The long strands of bootlace seaweed *Chorda filum* are often numerous on the middle shore. Another common seaweed of sheltered sites is *Fucus ceranoides* which is recorded from Barra and the west coast of Lewis. Most of the coast, however, is severely exposed and a rare wrack of rock ledges on the upper shore which can accept extreme exposure is *F. distichus anceps* recorded from the Butt of Lewis and the west coast of Islay.

The huge oar or tangleweeds flourish at the lower levels. Here again, some of this group require a degree of shelter and in very exposed conditions *Laminaria digitata*, a very common species, is replaced by the thongweed *Himanthalia elongata*. On even more exposed sites the long wavy tongues of *Alaria esculenta* are the characteristic fronds one can expect to find both in the Inner and Outer Isles. It is this seaweed which forms the conspicuous skirt at the base of Rockall. Other tangleweeds occurring are *Laminaria hyperborea*, *L. saccharina* and *Saccharina bulbosa*. These Laminarias are the basic material of a new industry which in recent years has become an important factor in the Hebridean economy.

The Sound of Harris is one of the localities where immense masses of tangleweed grow and is one of the main collection points. The tangleweed can only be gathered at suitable states of the tide and in practice cutting can only be done on five days in every fortnight; in addition, for each cutting day another day is needed for loading. The dependence on the tide, however, does mean that the crofter can satisfactorily dovetail his land work on the croft with this activity. The wet weed is taken to the factory at Sponish near Lochmaddy where it is dried and milled (losing three-quarters of its weight in the process), ready for transport to the mainland where it is used in the manufacture of many products including toothpaste, cosmetics, perfume and nylon. There are two more factories, one at Lochboisdale in South Uist and the other at Keose on Loch Erisort in Lewis.

The so-called red seaweeds grow at the lowest levels on the shore and are often exposed only at low tide apart from those which can be seen in the rock pools. There is quite a rich assemblage of species in the region. *Chondrus crispus*, *Rhodymenia palmata*, *Porphyra umbilicalis*, *Gigartina stellata*, *Laurencia pinnatifida* and *Lomentaria articulata* are commonly found. The first four are edible but it is doubtful whether they are eaten in the Hebrides today. *Psilota plumosa* is a small feathery dark red seaweed of northern distribution occurring in both the Inner and Outer Isles. An expedition to Barra in 1935 noted that the western coast was the richest in algae and recorded seventy-eight spp of seaweeds including at least one rare red species *Gelidium attenuata*. One of the most beautiful sights of seaweeds that I have come across was in Craighouse Bay on Jura; brown and

red fronds of infinitely varied pattern swayed gently to and fro
in sun-brightened lime-green water above a pink coralline-
encrusted sea floor.

The rich marine fauna of the Hebridean shores is located on
the rocky sections of the coastline, much of it in the various seaweed zones which give it protection. Amongst the most primitive of marine animals are the sponges which are often abundant
below low water mark. One such is a common purse sponge
Grantia compressa whose inch-long, pale-coloured tubes hang
downwards from rocks usually where certain red seaweeds are
found, although in Loch Maddy on North Uist it is recorded
from a belt of tangleweed. Another primordial group is that
of the so-called plant-animals to which the sea-firs belong. A
very common and well-distributed species is *Dynamena pumila*
whose tiny grey jointed triangles resemble more a string of
beads than a conifer. Richly coloured anemones live in rock
pools and from the middle shore downwards. If the available
information presents an accurate picture of the distribution
pattern then some individual species are very localised; a more
likely explanation is simply that sufficiently detailed surveys have
yet to be made. The lovely plumose anemone *Metridium senile*,
snakelocks *Anemonia sulcata* and *Sagartia elegans*, which lacks a
vernacular name, are recorded from North Uist and Barra and
are probably widespread in the Hebrides. The beadlet *Actinia
equina* is reported to be common on Barra and there too *Cereus
pedunculatus* is found which although generally plentiful in this
country was not known in the Outer Hebrides until the 1930s.
Acorn barnacles thrive on exposed rocky coasts and are probably
the commonest animal in this situation; in more sheltered conditions their numbers decline. *Chthamalus stellatus* a southern
species reaches at least as far as the south coast of Mull. The various
common crabs are numerous enough and on Muck in the spring
of 1938 three crab species were discovered which were virtually
unknown in the Hebrides although two of them are fairly common in south-western Britain. *Xantho incisus* is a small reddish-
brown crab living on the west coast of the island and the

commonest of the three; the hairy crab *Pilumnus hirtella* is of similar colour but rather smaller and the rarest is the smallest, only half an inch in width, *Pisimela denticulata*. Their presence on Muck is probably due to the Atlantic Drift although one would have expected to find them on at least some of the other Hebridean islands as well.

Limpets, mussels, dog whelks, periwinkles and top shells are characteristic inhabitants of rocky shores with the small periwinkle *Littorina neritoides* and the common mussel *Mytilus edulis* typical of the more exposed situations. In the Outer Hebrides the saddle oyster *Anomia ephippium* grows up to four times the average size. W. R. Hunter in a survey of the molluscan fauna of the Garvellochs noted that there was a restricted fauna on the hard, smooth quartzite compared with the softer limestone where rock-boring organisms such as *Hiatella striata* and the sponge *Cliona celata* had honeycombed the rock. Here were horse mussels *Modiolus modiolus*, pullet carpet shells *Venerupis pullastra* and young queen scallops *Chlamys opercularis*.

Starfish of various kinds are not infrequent at lower levels and several species of the tiny brittle-stars have been recorded from Barra. A green sea urchin of localised western distribution though fairly common in Ireland is *Paracentrotus lividus*; in the region it has been observed only on Muck presumably carried northwards in currents from Ireland. At the lowest levels sea-squirts are abundant although not all species have rocks as their habitat.

Flies infest the decayed masses of seaweed and phytophagous beetles frequent flowering plants. Carrion beetles can be observed feeding on dead marine animals and, not surprisingly, they include some with a definitely Scottish distribution such as *Staphylinus erythropterus* seen feeding on a dead crab on South Rona. A few spiders frequent rocky shores and an uncommon species *Halorates reprobus* has been recorded in seaweed on Kerrera. This is a truly maritime species of shore and saltmarsh but sometimes spiders of adjacent grassland will wander on to the shore. Grassy slopes behind rocky shores and boulder scree on some islands hold interesting insects. The grayling *Hipparchia semele* var *atlantica* flies amongst the rocks on Iona; the Rev J. H. Vine Hall suggests that this butterfly, which on the coast normally frequents dunes, probably moved to this new habitat because of the pressure of grazing on the machair. Several kinds of the day-flying burnets, some of them local or rare, are present on some of the Inner Hebrides notably on Mull and Skye. A careful search of the southern shores of Raasay might reveal the Oban burnet *Zygaena achilleae* a small colony of which was observed on the slopes of Beinn na Leac in 1933. The six-spot burnet *Z. filipendulae* which is regarded as the commonest burnet in Britain generally is less common in the Hebrides but it occurs on Mull, Ulva, Raasay and the west coast of Skye the caterpillars normally feeding on bird's-foot trefoil. The larvae of the variety *jocelynae* of the narrow-bordered five-spot burnet *Z. lonicerae*, a less common moth in the region, also feed on this and other trefoils on Skye's western coast. The slender Scotch burnet *Z. loti scotica* is recorded from the long, western sea lochs of Mull and from Ulva. Where the wild thyme *Thymus drucei* grows a Hebridean speciality the transparent burnet *Zygaena purpuralis* may be sought; there are records from Mull, Ulva, Gunna, Rhum, Sanday, Canna and Skye. The headquarters of this moth is in Ireland and this, therefore, is one of the insects indicative of Hebridean-Hibernian links.

Of the small passerines the rock pipit is the bird which one particularly associates with rocky shores and this is believed to be the commonest land bird on St Kilda. The birds in the Outer Isles differ from the British rock pipit in having practically no eyestripe, darker back and pale buff rather than pale yellow breast; they have been designated a separate sub-species *Meinertz-hageni*. The rock pipits on Skye are considered to be of intermediate type. In winter greenfinches are fond of congregating on the plant debris at the drift line. Turnstones are typical wading birds of rocky coasts and in a number of places non-breeding birds regularly summer. So far as I am aware there is as yet no satisfactory evidence of breeding but Dr Fraser Darling

believes that they may well breed on North Rona where the
Fianuis peninsula carries a population of about 200 turnstones.
The rather drab-coloured, purple sandpiper is another characteristic bird of rocky shores but it is only a winter visitor. More
common than either is the oyster-catcher which nests all along
the rocky shores although by no means confined to this habitat.
The seagull of the rocks is the herring gull which is numerous
and widespread. In winter these are joined by the occasional
glaucous gull arriving from the Arctic especially in the Outer
Hebrides and the odd bird may sometimes remain for the following summer; I have, for example, seen a second-year bird on
North Uist. Iceland gulls are similar but rarer winter visitors and
in the region are perhaps most likely to be seen on Lewis. Eiders,
which the islanders used to call the colk, are well distributed
along the coasts.

Mammal species are few but brown rats are all too common on
many islands and are frequent foragers along the shore finding
rich pickings in eggs, young birds and shellfish. The Shiant Isles
off the eastern coast of Harris have the black rat as well as the
brown species. It is ironic that one of the few islands which has
no rats today was in the past so plagued by them that it is
probable they were the indirect cause of the extermination of
the total human population. This island, uninhabited today, is
North Rona. The story of this tragic occurrence has been re-
counted a number of times but is worth repeating in its stark,
dramatic horror. There is no reason to doubt the truth of its
main outlines. Some thirty people were living on this remote
island in 1689, enduring extremely primitive conditions but not
suffering privation, enjoying a simple but serene existence.
Then a shipwreck brought what would almost certainly have
been black rats scurrying ashore in large numbers. There they
multiplied, devastating the islanders' meagre stores of food until
the people died of starvation for their very remoteness pre-
cluded them seeking food elsewhere. When the steward of the
island paid his annual visit and the boat nosed its way in for the
difficult landing he saw lying on the rocks the bodies of the last

North Ronans, a woman with a baby at her breast. The de-population of the Hebrides had begun. It was poetic justice that subsequently the rats themselves starved to death. That fierce carnivore, the feral mink, has not been slow in exploiting the food supplies on the rocky shores of Lewis and otters are well distributed though seldom seen.

ISLETS, STACKS AND SKERRIES

Scattered around virtually all the main islands and dotted about the Minch and the Atlantic far from other land are innumerable islets, stacks and skerries. Except for those on which lighthouse keepers live they are not often visited by anyone save the occasional lobster fisherman and more seldom still by naturalists but animals view them in an entirely different light. To tired migrants they represent welcome stopping-off places on long and hazardous journeys; for the seals they make ideal breeding grounds remote from human interference. There is in the region a certain amount of overlap in the distribution of the two British seals but some distinction of locality and habitat can be made. As a generalisation wild rocky coasts with caves attract the Atlantic grey seal while the common seal prefers sandbanks and estuaries. In the Hebrides, however, there cannot be any rigidity about this because sandbanks are few and the estuaries are rock-girt sea lochs. Dr L. Harrison Matthews in *British Mammals* points to a connection between breeding behaviour and habitat; common seal pups can enter the sea soon after birth whereas those of the grey seal cannot leave the birthplace until at least several days have elapsed. It is evident therefore that the latter has an especial need for inaccessible ledges and beaches safe from disturbance. The majority of their breeding stations are in the western part of the Outer Isles on Flodday near Barra, two of the Monach Isles, Causamul and Haskeir off North Uist, Shillay and Coppay in the Sound of Harris, Gasker and Kearstay off the western coast of Harris, St Kilda and the largest 'rookery' of all on North Rona with a population of several thousand adults.

There are a few breeding colonies in the Inner Hebrides on the two small islets of Eilean nan Ron and Eilean Ghaoideamal off Oronsay, the Treshnish Isles, Gunna, Horse Island near Muck and Oighsgeir near Canna. Some islanders consider there are differences between the seals of different colonies and although this might be a possibility more research needs to be done before this point can be decided. In view of the large distances that they travel outside the breeding season with consequent inter-mingling of stock this would seem to be very doubtful. In olden times the islands' inhabitants hunted seals for food, clothing and fuel; on Causamul, for example, as many as 320 seals have been killed in the autumn and there was a tradition that the local minister of the Church of Scotland was entitled to take all the young seals and these were called the Cullen-Mory, the Virgin Mary's seal. It has been estimated that by the end of the nine-teenth century the total Scottish population was down to a few hundred. In 1914 the Grey Seals Protection Act was passed pro-viding a close season during the breeding period. The popula-tion has increased greatly and there has been recent controversy over the damage which they are alleged to do to salmon fisheries. The shooting of grey seals is now permitted but only under Government licence. Common seals tend to haunt more accessible and sheltered places on the large islands; in the Outer Isles they are present in the Sound of Harris and on both west and east coasts; in the Inner Isles they frequent Mull and Skye. Notable breeding stations are the Crowlin Islands south-east of Raasay and along the western coast of Skye in Lochs Dunvegan and Bracadale.

South-east Islay has a very fragmented coastline with many detached portions of wave-surrounded rocks. Little vegetation grows other than seaweed, thrift and salt-sprayed turf but they provide favourite perching places for gulls and oyster-catchers, fulmars fly ceaselessly round them while eider and shelduck, and in the winter great northern divers and mergansers, swim in the sea below. Common and arctic terns find these offshore rocks ideal as undisturbed nesting sites. A similar assemblage of rocks lies in Craighouse Bay, Jura, and off the southern shore of Oronsay. Two of the latter group have already been mentioned as breeding places of the grey seal and one of them, Eilean nan Ron, which is Gaelic for seal island, is a notable haunt of barnacle geese in winter. Fifteen miles (24km) west of Colonsay is an underground extension of the Ross peninsula of Mull, the dolerite reef of Dubh Artach whose lighthouse is visible not only from Colonsay but on a very clear day from the summit of Ben More on Mull, thirty miles (48·27km) away. Eight miles (12·8km) or so to the north-west of Dubh Artach is another skerry based on a gneissose submarine reef; this is Skerryvore with an automatic lighthouse which is plainly visible from southern Tiree ten miles (16·1km) to the north. These lack land plants but are resting places for migrants where common winter visitors such as fieldfares and uncommon passage migrants such as barred warblers have been recorded.

Farther north is another skerry-based lighthouse but as this rock stands higher, some 34ft (10·4m) above the water, it has a more interesting flora and fauna. The rock itself, Oighsgeir, south-west of Canna, belongs to yet another geological formation, a pitchstone which probably flowed down the same ancient river which existed on the site of the Sgurr of Eigg. There are grasses and thrift and the presence of certain other wild flowers such as tormentil and bluebells strongly suggests that it was part of a much larger land mass in relatively recent geological history. In summer kittiwakes nest and during the autumn grey seals breed. In addition there are various species of Lepidoptera, common blue butterflies *Polyommatus icarus* and certain moths with grass eating larvae. The common ischnura damsel fly *Ischnura elegans* has been seen there in abundance and a form of a common whirligig beetle *Gyrinus natator sub-striatus* is numerous in a rock pool. Off northern Skye there are the Ascrib Islands in Loch Snizort and farther out the Fladda-chuain where varying numbers of terns and perhaps storm petrels nest.

Turning to the Outer Hebrides we find, south of Barra, various stacks and skerries including the stacks of Arnamul and

Lianamul off the western coast of Mingulay with large seabird populations. Causamul, which lies off Hougharry on North Uist, is a small skerry divided into two at high tide; grey seals find it a convenient hauling-out place and numbers breed while a variety of birds nest. Farther north, seven and a half miles (12·07km) due west of North Uist is the stack of Haskeir with an associated group of rocks a short distance away known as Haskeir Eagach. The islet has a low-lying central part and there are two natural tunnels going right through. Except in a dead calm, landing is not easy but adventurous naturalists nevertheless have landed. It is only thirty-four acres (13·7 hectares) but is another important grey seal station.

Skerries, seals and seaweed would be an alliterative but not inaccurate description of the Sound of Harris, an idyllic place on a fine summer day but tricky to navigate with shoals, reefs and cross-currents. Some five and a half miles (8·85km) west of Husinish Point in north Harris lies the forty-seven-acre (19·03 hectares) islet of Gasker. The plateau consists of grassland with many wild flowers. The island has been visited by two naturalists B. Roberts and R. Atkinson who reported massed beds of devil's bit scabious *Succisa pratensis* growing so luxuriantly that their leaves were like cos lettuce. This is yet another grey seal breeding ground and their wallowings have formed two large ponds whose muddy margins provide suitable conditions for rushes to thrive. In summer the air is filled with the cries of gulls, terns and oyster-catchers while from the sea comes the familiar crooning of the eider. It is probable that storm petrels nest and numbers of barnacle geese make the island their winter quarters. The many islets in Loch Roag, Lewis, are principally of interest to the birdwatcher for he may find here some of the more uncommon seabirds.

The remainder coming under this section are situated in the remotest parts of the British Isles. The Flannans, seventeen miles (27·35km) west of Lewis are the nearest to the Long Island but they are uninhabited save for the lighthouse keepers and are very difficult of access. They consist of seven islands and a number of stacks grouped in three clusters but the total area is less than one hundred acres (40·5 hectares). Their small size and remoteness ensures a sparse flora; only twenty-two plant species have been recorded of which thrift is perhaps the commonest being abundant in the grass on the cliff tops. Seabirds are plentiful and include some puffins. The colonisation of the group by fulmars began about the beginning of the century slowly increasing to the early 1950s since when the growth has been more rapid to over 2,000 pairs by 1959. The principal ornithological interest, however, is the large colony of Leach's fork-tailed petrel which nests on six of the Flannans. The starling is a fairly common resident. Occasional birds arrive on passage and two quail were seen in 1959. There are no rats but rabbits live on Eilean Mor. Sula Sgeir, Rockall and the stacks of the St Kilda group have been covered earlier in this chapter and in Chapter One.

COASTAL WATERS

To the peripatetic nature lover the coastal waters of the Hebrides are known only from the cabin of an aircraft or the deck of a steamer. If his visits are repeated enough he will see the Minch, or farther south the Sea of the Hebrides, in many moods; sullen rollers, surging swells, white crested waves, a myriad scintillating spangles, even a mirror-like surface and this more frequently than one might suppose. Out of sight beneath the waves there teems a wealth of life all of it, directly or indirectly, dependent on the surface plankton which is largely invisible save for the occasional phosphorescent glow.

Much of the multitudinous marine life is harvested by man. Clams or great scallops, prawns and lobsters are extensively gathered in both the Inner and Outer Isles and are processed at factories situated on Islay, Grimsay and Lewis. This is a relatively recent development which together with other schemes has brought a measure of prosperity to the islanders. In places like North Uist, for example, where there was extreme poverty in the early years of this century, there is now a general air of well-being. Despite local fluctuations, herrings of superb quality still shoal in vast numbers in Hebridean waters especially in the Atlantic west of the Outer Hebrides. Other fish of the region well known to the housewife include cod, haddock, hake, halibut, mackerel and skate and there are many other species. The large deepwater fish ling which has a distinct partiality for cod as food is perhaps not quite so well known; it is reported scarce in the Inner Hebrides but is found in some quantity between St Kilda and the Rockall Bank. An inshore fish of northern waters is the coalfish or saithe which abounds off rocky Hebridean shores. Its close relative the pollack or lythe is generally regarded as a more southerly species but in this region at any rate its distribution overlaps that of the saithe and it occurs in the same habitat right up to northern Lewis. The largest fishes are the sharks several species of which frequent Hebridean waters. The tope, porbeagle and thresher sharks feed on other fish but strangely the largest species in these waters, the basking shark, feeds only on plankton. This giant fish can grow up to 40ft (12·2m) in length although 30ft (9·1m) is more usual. Their livers are rich in oil and in the past they have been hunted for this, the latest enterprise being a factory on Soay adjacent to Skye where shark fishing was carried on for a while from 1946. This is probably still the commonest shark in the Minch and is certainly the one which makes itself conspicuous by its habit of basking on the surface but there are reports that it is not as plentiful as it used to be.

A considerable variety of whales visit Hebridean waters during the summertime but great expertise is needed to identify them and many a holidaymaker would count himself fortunate if he could distinguish between a basking shark and a whale. One feature which can be helpful is the former's habit of straight submergence as opposed to the characteristic roll of the latter. Porpoises and dolphins are small whales which travel in parties or schools and are quite plentiful around the islands. There are several species of dolphins visiting the Minch principally the common, Risso's and bottle-nosed. Large herds of pilot whales are occasionally sighted and to some Hebrideans they are known as blackfish. Another medium-sized species is that ferocious animal the killer whale, the only one which regularly feeds on warm-blooded mammals such as seals, on occasion even attacking its own kind. The very tall dorsal fin of the adult male is a conspicuous identification feature. Some of the really large whales are fairly regular visitors including the blue rorqual, the largest mammal in the world which grows to more than 80ft (24·4m) in length. Cuvier's whale is probably not uncommon in the region and specimens have been stranded in recent years on Colonsay and Jura.

The North Atlantic Drift brings more than mild weather to the region. A miscellany of floating objects including occasional material from the West Indies such as beans, coconuts, seeds and shells periodically arrives on the western shores. The tropical by-the-wind-sailor *Velella spirans*, a relative of the jellyfish and of bizarre appearance with its miniature blue-edged 'sail', is carried to the coasts of Muck and Canna. The violet sea snail *Janthina* sp is a pelagic surface-dwelling mollusc which is carried immense distances by the current and has been recorded from Pabbay in the Sound of Harris and from Muck. These currents may also have some influence on the movement of shoals of fish into the coastal waters.

The variety of birds which travellers may see in Hebridean waters depends mainly on the season but to some extent also on the locality. Much remains to be discovered about the distribution of birds along the coast in winter for few ornithologists visit the islands at this time. At any time of the year one can travel with an air of expectancy for there is always a possibility of seeing one of the more uncommon seabirds. Apart from the camp followers, the gulls which assiduously trail the steamer, a watch from the rails during a summer crossing of the Minch will reveal parties of auks hastening across the water, the effortless glide of fulmars, the occasional gannet plummeting into the waves, a great skua harrying a gull and possibly a flight of storm petrels. Near the breeding haunts of Manx shearwaters, for

Plate 9 (above) The Harp Rock, Lunga, in the Treshnish Isles, a haunt of seabirds
Plate 10 (below) Puffin on Mingulay

Plate 11 (above) Purple saxifrage on the Oa peninsula, Islay
Plate 12 (below) Clisham, Harris, the highest hill in the Outer Hebrides
with willow bushes in the foreground

example off the Small Isles and between the Treshnish Isles and Tiree, these birds will be seen in their distinctive flight skimming the waves. By good fortune rarer birds may be seen. The great shearwater is an occasional summer and autumn visitor and is more likely to be seen in this region than anywhere else in Britain particularly west of the Outer Hebrides. It has been recorded a number of times in the vicinity of Rockall and I like to think that the mysterious Rockall Jack of the nineteenth-century fishermen was this species although I believe some consider it to be the fulmar which is the commonest bird of that area. Autumn is the time to visit such promontories as the Butt of Lewis to watch for movements of passage migrants. In favourable conditions there may be a procession of Manx, great and sooty shearwaters and numbers of skuas, great and arctic with an occasional pomarine. The rarest of this genus in the Hebrides is the long-tailed but it has been recorded from the Outer Isles and is more frequent around Rockall where the other three species also occur. Generally speaking, the Outer Isles are better for the more uncommon seabirds.

In winter various seabirds and waterfowl take up their residence in the coastal waters of the region moving closer in to shore in rough weather. Their numbers fluctuate considerably from year to year and place to place but the normal components of this community are divers, more especially great northern divers, grebes, particularly slavonian and little grebes and various duck including mergansers, eider, scaup, long-tailed, golden-eye and wigeon. It should be added that all of these species are not necessarily found together in any one locality. Perhaps the largest numbers of wintering scaup are on Islay where I have seen large rafts on Loch Indaal although they are present on certain other islands in both the Inner and Outer Isles. Long-tailed duck are recorded from the Gigha–Jura area, off the western coasts of the Uists and in north-east Lewis. Scoter are strangely uncommon in the Western Isles but they are reported from the Sound of Harris and the Stornoway area and the occasional velvet scoter is seen. Mallard, which one thinks of as

F

essentially a freshwater species will sometimes resort to the sea and I have seen numbers in the autumn off the western coast of Tiree. If the birdwatcher is extremely fortunate there could be a chance of seeing one of the very rare ducks such as the king eider or the even rarer Steller's eider a drake of which was present for many months on South Uist from 1972 onwards. Glaucous and Iceland gulls frequent the Long Island coast in very small numbers during the winter. The little auk is an irregular winter visitor which is occasionally seen off the Inner Isles; this species, however, most frequently comes to notice when in severe gales 'wrecks' of these birds are driven far inland and found in the most unlikely places. Mute and whooper swans visit some of the sheltered sea lochs. In 1918 F. S. Beveridge on North Uist referred to the Bewick swan's partiality for salt water and stated that flocks of a hundred or so were commonplace but since that time they have disappeared from the whole region.

The ever present possibility of oil spillage remains an extremely serious hazard in a region where such vast numbers of seabirds are congregated. After the massive kill in the Irish sea in 1969 a heavy decline in the breeding population of the Hebrides was noted the following year. A survey on Canna, for example, showed that a shag colony of 1,000 pairs had declined to less than 150 pairs. In October 1969 an oil spillage on Loch Indaal on Islay resulted in the deaths of at least 450 eider, merganser, scaup, scoter and guillemot. Eider were the most affected and badly oiled birds of this species were seen walking as much as half a mile inland; this is most abnormal behaviour and reveals considerable disorientation.

CHAPTER FOUR

The coastline continued

Shingle beaches—Sandy beaches—Sand dunes—
Saltmarshes

SHINGLE BEACHES

IN THIS SECTION THE word 'shingle' has a wide connotation ranging from fine pea gravel to boulders. There are many shingle beaches scattered throughout the region. Many of these consist of belts of shingle backing sandy shores and frequently the stones are of the large size, 10–30cm, known as cobbles. Large boulders are sometimes accumulated high on the beach as in western Mull and the narrow inlets of western Rhum. Winter gales transport pebbles from one locality to another and storm shingle amassed on the west coast of Benbecula has been described as amongst the most spectacular conglomerations of its kind in Britain. Gravel is removed from some beaches on Lewis for commercial purposes. This is an operation which if carried to excess can cause dangerous erosion and the quantity excavated is controlled by Coast Protection Orders. The numerous raised beaches are a type of 'fossil' shore. Most of them have long been covered with vegetation and must be regarded as part of the adjacent habitat but in a few places their original nature is quite evident as on Jura where the barren quartzite pebbles have little plant cover.

From a distance a belt of shingle will often appear bereft of vegetation nor is this surprising when one considers the slender quantity of soil available at surface level from which plants could derive nourishment. There is a certain amount of minerals and humus from wind-blown sand and rotting seaweed which lodge between the interstices of the pebbles but a number of plants obtain their sustenance by sending down long tap roots to lower levels. A closer approach, therefore, will reveal rather more flowers than one might at first expect. Plants are often isolated and there are large stretches without any but, here and there, a particular flower will establish a firm foothold and carpet the ground forming an almost pure plant association.

It may be that the first objects to catch the eye are the long upright narrow leaves of the curled dock *Rumex crispus* with their incurved margins. Or attention may be drawn to a mat of silver dotted with yellow flowers and spreading by means of runners over the shingle; this is silverweed *Potentilla anserina*. On the western coast of Mull these two species grow together on boulders and both are well distributed in the islands generally. The white-rayed flowers of scentless mayweed *Tripleurospermum maritimum* are plentiful enough in places both in the fleshy coastal form *maritimum* and also *inodorum*. The sea campion *Silene maritima* with its inflated bladder of sepals is more typical of rocky shores but it is reported from shingle on Lewis, Raasay and all the Small Isles. Raasay has herb Robert *Geranium robertianum* growing in abundance amongst the pebbles although crevices in walls and shady rocks are more characteristic haunts. Three widespread plants which grow both on sand and shingle are sea rocket *Cakile maritima*, Babington's orache *Atriplex glabriuscula* var *babingtonii* and sea sandwort *Honkenya peploides*. The first and last of these are perhaps more common on sand but are found on a few Hebridean shingle beaches. Cleavers *Galium aparine*, that common seed-clinging plant of hedgerows, grows amongst beach pebbles on Tiree, Gunna, Coll and Rhum.

The upper levels of shingle would generally be regarded as an arid habitat apart from the salt spray but occasionally moist hollows exist under the stones enabling moisture-loving plants to obtain a foothold. Two such are water pepper *Polygonum hydropiper*, whose drooping flower spikes can be seen amongst the boulders of Mull, and the coastal form of skullcap, *Scutellaria galericulata* var *littoralis*, which grows plentifully on the beaches of Scalpay, Raasay, Rona and Rhum. The speciality of the region is the oyster plant *Mertensia maritima* which has become scarce in this century but is recorded from Mull, Islay, Iona, the Treshnish Isles, Coll, Eigg, Sanday and the Monachs. One of the adverse factors affecting this plant is the damage done by winter storms; for example, high tides during the winter of 1974/5 plucked up quantities of the *Mertensia* community on the Treshnish Isles.

The unstable and barren nature of the habitat and the relatively small amounts of vegetation account for the scarcity of invertebrate life. Some encrusting marine organisms attach themselves to the pebbles and a few arthropods such as sandhoppers *Gammarus* spp and the sea slater *Ligia oceanica* find shelter in the interstices. The shore crab *Carcinus maenas* is ubiquitous in all coastal habitats and is found under stones. The fact that many Hebridean shingle beaches exist behind sandy stretches means that occasionally invertebrates of such habitats are found on the shingle. So, for example, the lead-coloured spider wasp *Pompilus plumbeus*, an insect of coastal sand which preys on spiders, has been observed on Raasay shingle and caterpillars of the small rivulet *Perizoma alchemillata*, a moth of lanes and woods, feed here on hemp nettle at the upper margins of the shingle. Where there are small rock pools the tiny insect *Lipura maritima* which skates on the water surface will sometimes desert the pool for the adjacent shingle and it has been so noted under stones on the western coast of North Uist. Various species of flies frequent the driftline of decaying seaweed.

Birds associated with shingle are few. Ringed plovers and oyster-catchers lay their eggs in a hollow, often unlined, amongst the stones. Terns will nest in several kinds of marine habitat including shingle. The 1969/70 seabird census known as 'Operation Seafarer' disclosed that 1,200 pairs of arctic, 76 pairs of common and 66 pairs of little terns nested in the Outer Hebrides. The overwhelming preponderance of arctic terns is

striking and contrasts with Islay where common terns outnumber arctic. Little terns are scarce but nest in a number of
scattered localities in the Inner and Outer Isles. A few turnstones may stay as non-breeders throughout the summer and the
1972 Scottish Bird Report records that three were observed in
display flight on Oronsay on 28 May. They are present throughout the winter when they are joined by purple sandpipers.

SANDY BEACHES

Shores of sand far surpass those of shingle and the vast stretches
in the Outer Hebrides are some of the most magnificent in the
British Isles. There are many fine beaches in the Inner Isles too
and the Laggan strand over five miles long skirting the outer
reaches of Loch Indaal on Islay is one of the largest. Many of
these sandy shores are situated on the western side of both
island groups and embayed in a rocky coastline. There are some
exceptions to this, Tiree, Lewis, some islands in the Sound of
Harris, Barra and Mingulay have sandy bays on the east but
they are few in relation to the general pattern. There is some
variety in the type of sand. The basaltic lavas of Mull produce in
places on the south and west coast a grey sand and near Duntulm
at the northern tip of Skye there is an unusual beach of green
sand consisting of over eighty per cent of the mineral olivine.
Skye too, on the eastern side of Loch Dunvegan, has small
patches of sand composed of dry broken pieces of the calcium-
coated *Lithothamnion calcareum*. The well known 'singing' sands
at Laig Bay on Eigg can only be heard in certain circumstances;
a good time is during a spell of calm, dry weather. Many of the
beaches especially in the Outer Isles are composed of shell-sand
whose calcium content varies greatly but averages fifty per cent.
The intensity of the light on these beaches is such that the whole
scene has a bleached effect like an over-exposed colour trans-
parency.

Sandy shores do not have many more wild flowers than have
shingle ones but it is a different flora with little overlap. I have

seen remarkably fine clumps of sea rocket on Tiree sand and this species occurs elsewhere in the Inner Hebrides although it is not very common; it is more plentiful in the Outer Hebrides. The flowers of this plant attract numbers of insects in the summer. Sea holly *Eryngium maritimum* is quite a handsome umbellifer with its glaucous foliage and blue flowers but although it is reported from some islands including Islay, Iona, Coll, Tiree, Barra and Mingulay it does not seem very common in the region. Other typical species present with varying frequency and irregular distribution are saltwort *Salsola kali*, sea sandwort, frosted orache *Atriplex laciniata*, and Babington's orache. A creeping plant known in the region only from Eriskay and Vatersay is the sea bindweed *Calystegia soldanella*. The well known tradition that seeds were sown by Bonnie Prince Charlie is based solely on the fact that Eriskay was the first Scottish soil on which he landed. There is no reason to suppose that he had any interest in botany nor is it much more likely that the seeds were accidentally transported by himself or his retinue.

The marine life is more in evidence than on the shingle although many molluscs live in shallow offshore water rather than on the shore itself. Numbers of mollusc shells can be collected on the beach and on Melbost sands in Lewis they occur in heaps. Two of the most typical and most abundant are the thin tellin *Tellina tenuis* and the common cockle *Cardium edule*. The latter are so numerous on Barra that they have given their name to the Cockle Strand otherwise Traigh Mhor and a small industry exists both for processing the shells for grit and for selling the shellfish itself. A common and characteristic bivalve of the lower sand on exposed shores is the banded wedge shell *Donax vittatus* but in conditions of extreme exposure not even this mollusc is present. Others include the Baltic tellin *Macoma balthica*, oval venus *Venus ovata*, striped venus *V. striatula*, pullet carpet shell *Tapes pullata*, gapers *Mya* spp, razor shells *Ensis* spp and netted dog whelk *Nassarius reticulatus*. The tiny laver spire shell *Peringia ulvae* and the sea slug *Alderia modesta* are normally inhabitants of saltmarshes or muddy estuaries but due to the brackish character of the inlets on the western coast of North Uist they are recorded from the sands of Clachan. A few uncommon and rare shells occur within the region. A new species of spire shell *Hydrobia neglecta* has been discovered in North Uist in recent years; a rare tellin *Tellin brittanica* lives on sand on Skye, South Uist and north-east Lewis; an uncommon tiny white shell *Neolepta sulcatum* is found on Benbecula and a rare needle whelk *Centhiopsis tubercularis* has been recorded from the low-water mark on Barra. A few species of bristle worms inhabit the Hebridean sands, notably the lug worm *Arenicola marina*, cat worms *Nephthys* spp, the variegated ragworm *Nereis diversicolor*, peacock worm *Lanice conchilega* and a bright orange-red worm *Scoloplos armiger*.

As on shingle nesting birds are few being virtually restricted to terns, ringed plovers and oyster-catchers. Gulls and shelduck use the beaches as resting places and in winter duck and geese visit the shore particularly the areas of muddy sand. At migration times, however, more birds frequent the sand than the shingle. White wagtails are fairly common spring passage migrants in the Outer Hebrides and some of the Inner Isles occasionally remaining to breed. The wader which is especially typical of Hebridean strands during the autumn passage is the sanderling which can easily be picked out from other waders by the whiteness of its plumage and its rapid runs as it incessantly searches for food. Others include black and bar-tailed godwits, dunlin, little stint, turnstone, curlew, whimbrel, redshank and greenshank. The one mammal frequently seen on the sand is the rabbit in areas where dunes abut on the beach and on islands which have them brown rats forage along the shoreline.

SAND DUNES

There are many extensive and superb dune systems in the Hebrides. Most of the Inner Isles have dunes but for the finest development one must go to the Long Island where dunes stretch along most of the western coastline and in parts of the east as well. The entire island of Berneray in the Sound of Harris is virtually a sand dune in itself and the same might be said of the Monachs. The sandhills form in successive belts one behind each other like waves of a golden sea. Very occasionally these rolling waves are truncated by a perpendicular cliff dividing the beach from the dunes as at Laggan strand on Islay where there is a steep sandy cliff about 20ft (6·1m) high. The dunes here are almost a mile in depth and well covered with vegetation.

While the general pattern is for a gradual build up of the sandhills the reverse process sometimes takes place. In the northern part of Barra the dunes between the beaches of Traigh Eais on the west and Traigh Mhor on the east are breaking up and steps have been taken to arrest this deterioration. A drastic extension of this procedure occurs when through a combination of insufficient binding material such as marram and violent winds, a blow-out happens and whirling grains of sand are tossed out of a hollow. A blow-out of serious proportions befell old dunes at Bornish on South Uist in 1950. An unsuccessful attempt to stop further erosion was made in 1955 by which time the area involved was eight acres (3·2 hectares). Four years later another attempt to stabilise the dune failed. The eroded area had grown to forty acres (16·2 hectares) by 1964 and a large-scale effort was called for. The services of the army were enlisted and the whole site was levelled. The work of forming a stable surface began again. Marram plants were laboriously planted by hand and intersown with a variety of other grasses. The work proceeded throughout the two following years and within a few years a large degree of stability had resulted. When fixed dunes become carpeted with a wide array of dwarf plants they are known as machair and form a vital part of the crofting system. Although it is not easy to make a clear-cut distinction between the dunes and the machair because they grade into one another the latter will in general be dealt with in Chapter Seven.

Behind the scattered plants of the foreshore the embryo dune begins to form with marram *Ammophila arenaria* and, generally to a much lesser extent, with sand couch *Agropyron junceiforme*. These are able to withstand salt better than other grasses. Occasional plants of sand fescue *Festuca rubra* var *arenaria*, with its markedly glaucous leaves, dark green chickweed *Cerastium atrovirens* and ragwort *Senecio jacobaea* invade the sand. A sparse growth of lyme grass *Elymus arenarius* is recorded throughout the Outer Hebrides but in the Inner Isles it grows only on Eigg and Skye.

As these mobile dunes develop a considerable variety of flowers begin colonising. They include the bloody cranesbill *Geranium sanguineum* which abounds on the Coll dunes and grows also on Tiree, Iona and the Treshnish Isles; the attractive little storksbill *Erodium cicutarium*; sand meadow rue *Thalictrum minus arenarium* a dune plant of chiefly northern distribution; kidney vetch *Anthyllis vulneraria*; bird's foot trefoil *Lotus corniculatus*; wild carrot *Daucus carota*, lady's bedstraw *Galium verum*; sand sedge *Carex arenaria* and many others. A very rare clover of southern distribution was discovered on Coll in 1939. This is *Trifolium bocconei* known elsewhere in the British Isles only from a Cornish locality and Jersey. The dune association is in fact made up of an amalgam of several habitat types, waste ground, calcareous soils, sandy soils, neutral grassland as well as more specifically dune species.

In the moist hollows known as slacks, between the ridges, several species of orchids are often present, sometimes in abundance. The variety of early marsh orchid inhabiting dunes is *Dactylorchis incarnata* var *coccinea*, a rich red in contrast to the flesh colour of the type. The Irish marsh orchid *D. majalis occidentalis* grows in dune slacks in North and South Uist, Coll and Tiree. The Hebridean orchid *D. fuchsii hebridensis* which is a sub-species of the common spotted orchid is also found in the slacks although it is more plentiful on the fixed dunes. The frog orchid *Coeloglossum viride* occurs in some places. Other flowering plants of these hollows include the knotted pearlwort *Sagina nodosa*, red bartsia *Odontites verna*, lesser spearwort *Ranunculus flammula* and a moss *Acrocladium cuspidatum* which is particularly plentiful on the Monachs slacks.

The inner dunes have an increase of grasses and white clover *Trifolium repens* the latter playing an important stabilising role on exposed dunes. Orchids such as the pyramidal *Anacamptis pyramidalis* are more numerous together with daisies *Bellis perennis* and many mosses. The normal tendency for the innermost dune to become acidic is not very pronounced in the Hebrides but a community of ling has developed behind the Laggan strand on Islay and a conifer plantation has been established.

One of the most notable moths of the dunes is the belted beauty *Nyssia zonaria*, an insect with a western distribution occurring in Wales, Ireland and north-west England. In Scotland its presence, sometimes in abundance, on a number of the Hebridean islands has been taken as an indication of former land connections with Ireland. This theory has the more force in that the female is wingless. The parallel stripes on the wings of the male give it a handsome appearance but it is seldom seen by visitors for it flies in March and April. The larvae feed on a variety of foliage throughout the summer; on South Uist during one season it is recorded that it was impossible to sit down on the sandhills without crushing these caterpillars and I have found them extremely numerous behind Seal Bay, Barra. The treble-bar *Anaites plagiata* is a light-coloured moth with transverse bars on the forewings whose typical haunt is coastal sandhills; it has been noted on Barra and probably is to be found on other islands. Other dune moths are the Portland moth *Ochropleura praecox*, white-line dart *Euxoa tritici*, the grass rivulet *Perizoma albulata*, and the coast dart *Agrotis cursoria* which flies in late summer over the sandhills. The common blue *Polyommatus icarus*, meadow brown *Maniola jurtina* and grayling *Hipparchia semele* are the typical butterflies of the dunes. On a few of the Outer Isles, that is on Vatersay, Barra, South Uist and Baleshare, a more brightly coloured sub-species of the meadow brown var *splendida* exists but elsewhere the butterfly appears to be the type.

In the beetles, weevils are often numerous. *Otiorrhynchus*

atroapterus is an 8mm black weevil which though local on the mainland is the characteristic beetle of the Barra sandhills. When camping on North Uist dunes I had the interior of the tent covered with hordes of the tiny black weevil *Apion* sp probably *apricans* which sometimes reaches pest proportions in clover. Ground beetles of the family Carabidae are common as are the ladybird beetles especially the two-spot *Adalia punctata*. A plant bug of dry sandy places with as yet comparatively few records in Scotland is *Nysius thymi*; this has been noted as numerous on thyme on the dunes of Rhum although despite its specific name it is not always restricted to thyme. Several species of bumble bees fly on the dunes but the most numerous is *Bombus smithianus*. A solitary bee which makes its burrows in the soft sand is *Colletes floralis*; it has a scattered western distribution in Ireland, south-west Scotland and the Hebrides where it has been identified on Colonsay, Tiree, Pabbay and Barra. This, therefore, is another species indicative of Irish land connections. The harvestman *Phalangium opilio* is sometimes numerous. Earthworms are often abundant on the machair and are present also on the dunes. This might seem surprising in view of the earthworms' need for moisture but they are able to find this in the slacks and under dung. The calcareous sand provides a fertile habitat for land snails and of these the pale brown turreted snail *Cochlicella acuta* is especially typical of dunes occurring in both island groups but there are a number of other kinds including the well known garden snail *Helix aspersa*.

The greatest variety of birds are found in the inner dunes and will therefore be referred to in Chapter Seven. Skylarks sing over the sandhills and are one of the most numerous species. In the summer wheatears arrive to nest in the rabbit burrows and partridges have been reported nesting on the dunes of Coll. Birds of neighbouring habitats will occasionally wander into this zone attracted by some tasty morsels of food—birds such as starlings from the crofts, herring gulls from the shore and hoodies from the moor. In some of the marshy spots in the Outer Isles snipe and dunlin nest. Red deer have been observed on the Kilmory dunes on Rhum feeding on the puff ball *Calvatia caelata*. Rabbits breed and are often present in great numbers although outbreaks of myxomatosis temporarily reduce their numbers.

SALT MARSHES

A thin belt of rather impoverished saltmarsh exists in a number of places along the coasts on Islay, Colonsay, Mull, Iona, Coll, Rhum, Canna, Skye with adjacent islands and several of the main islands in the outer group. At the head of sea inlets such as Lochs Gruinart and Indaal on Islay and the great lochs of Skye the saltmarsh area is much more extensive. The soil base of these marshes is normally mud or sandy mud but at Melbost in eastern Lewis the saltmarsh has developed on shell-sand and on Mull and Canna there is a foundation of shingle under some marshes which enables the buck's horn plantain *Plantago corono-pus* to thrive on the last-named island. The areas of short turf with sea plantain *P. maritima* and thrift *Armeria maritima*, two of the commonest plants on many of the marshes, would hardly be recognised as saltmarsh by the casual onlooker although the latter makes a colourful display in June at places such as the Seile-bost saltings on Harris.

There is a certain but by no means constant or consistent zonation. The saltmarsh grass *Puccinellia maritima* and glasswort *Salicornia europaea* are usually the initial colonisers at the lowest levels; the former is particularly plentiful in the southern part of the Inner Hebrides and less common farther north and the latter is widespread but of sparse occurrence. The middle levels have the greatest number of plants with usually the sea plantain domi-nant. Colour is provided by the trailing stems of the pink-flowered sea milkwort *Glaux maritima*, the button heads of thrift, the sea spurreys *Spergularia marina* and *S. media* and the mauve flowers of sea aster *Aster tripolium*. The last named is abundant on Islay and Jura but is much scarcer farther north al-though it is locally plentiful in the Outer Isles where at Gress on Lewis a dwarf form of this plant has been recorded.

Most of the plants of the saltmarsh are, it must be admitted, unattractive in appearance but they do not lack interest to the botanist. Sea arrow-grass *Triglochin maritima* although a mono-cotyledon is not a true grass; it has fleshier leaves than its relative of fresh marshes and bears its greenish-brown flowers in late summer. The saltmud rush *Juncus gerardii* is a characteristic rush which often occupies drier spots within the marsh. The red or narrow blysmus *Blysmus rufus* is a small club rush which although within the British Isles is of north-western distribution appears to follow the general trend of being less common in the northern Hebrides. The low-growing annual sea-blite *Suaeda maritima* and the tall parsley water dropwort *Oenanthe lachenalii* occur in a number of places. At the higher levels there are scurvy grasses *Cochlearia officinalis* and *C. scotica*, various pasture grasses and sedges. On the Loch Indaal marsh there is even gorse on the drier parts.

A few insects have adapted themselves to the hazards of life on the saltings with its periodic inundations from the tide. One such is the eleven-spot ladybird beetle *Coccinella 11-punctata* with black spots on orange-red wing cases somewhat similar to the familiar seven-spot ladybird but distinctly smaller. The eleven-spot ladybird found on these Hebridean marshes is a northern form var *boreolitoralis*. The shorebug *Salda littoralis* is an insect with principally a northern distribution; its main habitat is silty river margins but it is occasionally to be found in saltmarshes within the region as at Dry Harbour on South Rona, Canna and elsewhere. Various species of pond-skaters swim on the surface of the brackish water in small pools. The laver spire shell *Peringia ulvae* is a common inhabitant of the numerous gullies which are part of the typical physical pattern of the saltings. At higher levels in rather less saline water the related Jenkin's spire shell *Potamopyrgus jenkinsii* is reported to be well established in the Outer Isles.

The narrowness of the zone generally and the small amount of cover supplied means that there is no distinctive bird life. Various waders, particularly redshank and lapwing, and wildfowl frequent the tidal pools and brackish creeks throughout most of the year. In winter several species of geese crop the vegetation including the vast hordes of barnacles on Islay although they do not of course restrict themselves to this habitat. The succulent vegetation is much sought after by mammals, principally rabbits but also hares and in some localities even deer. This combined with heavy grazing from wildfowl and domestic cattle results in close-cropped turf.

CHAPTER FIVE

Aquatic habitats

Rivers–Lochs

INEVITABLY, HEBRIDEAN RIVERS ARE small and short. Many of them are only one or two miles in length although a few are much longer; in some places such as on Skye and along the eastern coast of Mull the burns drop vertically over precipitous cliffs to the sea. The east-flowing rivers of the Outer Hebrides were once minor tributaries of the great river that flowed along the channel of the Minch. Despite their small size the burns with their banks and marshy valleys hold much of interest.

In small fast-flowing streams flowering plants are unlikely to be present and none of the Soay (Skye) burns have plants at all. In general, however, there is rather more vegetation than one might expect. The long dull green submerged strands of the willow moss *Fontinalis antipyretica* are anchored to mid-stream rocks. Many streams after leaving the steep hill slopes come to flatter sections where the slower flow enables aquatic vegetation to become established. One of the commonest of the submerged plants, particularly in the Outer Hebrides, is alternate-flowered water milfoil *Myriophyllum alterniflorum*, the thin filmy masses moving sinuously below the surface. An American form, var *americanum*, has been identified on Tiree. Pondweeds are more typical of still waters but in a few sluggish burns the genus is represented by the bog pondweed *Potamogeton polygonifolius*, floating pondweed *P. natans* and reddish pondweed *P. alpinus* a local species which is very scarce in the Hebrides but which together with a rare hybrid *P. prussicus* has been recorded from

Plate 13 (above) Red stag on Jura's southern coast with Islay in the background
Plate 14 (below) Sea rocket on Traigh Bhaigh, Tiree

Plate 15 (above) Common seals on a skerry in Loch Dunvegan, Skye
Plate 16 (below) Wild goats on Islay

a Colonsay burn. The edible watercress *Rorippa nasturtium-aquaticum* is plentiful on many islands and water starworts *Callitriche* spp are widespread especially in the small rivulets and ditches. The floating club rush *Eleogiton fluitans* which one perhaps associates more particularly with moorland pools, is well distributed in streams throughout the Outer Hebrides.

A certain amount of emergent vegetation grows along the shallow water of the edges but it must be emphasised once more that there is considerable variety in the constitution of plant communities from island to island. The floating sweet grass *Glyceria fluitans* and the lesser spearwort *Ranunculus flammula* with its var *scoticus* are widespread. Reedmace *Typha latifolia* which is so common in England is very rare in the Hebrides but it has been observed growing in a small river in western Lewis. Other emergent water plants growing in scattered localities are the common reed *Phragmites australis*, branched bur-reed *Sparganium erectum*, lesser water plantain *Baldellia ranunculoides*, brooklime *Veronica beccabunga* which is found in small burns and ditches and water pepper *Polygonum hydropiper*. Where some of the rivers enter the sea there grows a grass characteristic of this habitat, the water whorl-grass *Catabrosa aquatica*. This is a distinctly uncommon species and is becoming scarcer perhaps because it is much sought after by cattle wherever they are able to gain access to it.

A greater variety of plants is found on the rocky banks and in the adjoining marshes. Fine clumps of royal fern *Osmunda regalis* are well distributed where there are moist conditions such as wet ledges where the creeping willow *Salix repens* is also found. During the spring the banks of a number of streams in both the Inner and Outer Isles are clothed in places with the pink flowers of butterbur *Petasites hybridus*. Other flowers of streamsides include yellow flag *Iris pseudacorus*, purple loosestrife *Lythrum salicaria*, angelica *Angelica sylvestris* and monkey flower *Mimulus guttatus* the last named is naturalised along the burns of Eigg.

Most of the foregoing also grow in the freshwater marshes with many other flowers many of them very colourful in sum-

G

mer. There is the yellow of marsh marigold *Caltha palustris*; the white of bog stitchwort *Stellaria alsine* and hemlock water dropwort *Oenanthe crocata*; the creamy-white of meadowsweet *Filipendula ulmaria*; the lilac of marsh violet *Viola palustris*; the pink of marsh willow herb *Epilobium palustre* and ragged robin *Lychnis flos-cuculi* and the brown-red of marsh cinquefoil *Potentilla palustris*. The blue-eyed grass *Sisyrinchium bermudiana* of western Ireland, which is not a true grass, has an isolated station in the Hebrides on marshy ground on Coll. The very rare holy grass *Hierochloe odorata* is a true perennial grass and in the British Isles it is known only from a few widely-scattered localities; in the region it is found only on Benbecula. A few orchids grow in marshy ground and are sometimes quite numerous; they include the heath spotted orchid *Dactylorchis ericetorum*, dwarf purple orchid *D. purpurella* and the early marsh orchid *D. incarnata* with its distinctive flesh-pink colour.

Only one butterfly is widespread throughout the Hebrides on marshy ground and margins of rivers and that is the green-veined white *Pieris napi*. The marsh fritillary *Euphydryas aurinia* is typical of this habitat but as elsewhere in Britain it has a localised distribution and is known only from Islay, Jura, Gunna, Tiree and Rhum. The caterpillars feed on devil's bit *Scabiosa succisa* and hibernate in silky webs attached to the leaves. The 'woolly bear' caterpillars of the garden tiger moth *Arctia caja* can be seen on a variety of plants; on Benbecula they have been noted on water mint and on South Uist on pondweed although the moth itself is not a marsh insect.

Few studies have been made of the aquatic life of Hebridean streams so that it is not possible to present a comprehensive picture. The golden-ringed dragonfly *Cordulegaster boltonii* is found in both the Inner and Outer Isles. The nymph is the only one likely to be found in swift-flowing mountain streams where it buries itself in the stream bed. Boggy streams may have the nymphs of the darter dragonfly, the northern emerald *Somatochlora arctica*, but in the region this rare boreo-alpine insect has been recorded only from Rhum. Caddis and stonefly larvae are other inhabitants of the burns. The larvae of the former are principally those which are either free-swimming or live in silken tunnels. One such web-spinning species of fast-flowing burns is *Philopotamus montanus* noted as widespread on Rhum. The caddis larvae which build themselves a portable home consisting of a tube of stones or mollusc shells cemented together generally live in still water or very slow-flowing streams but an exception to this is in the species which belong to the genus *Agapetus* whose stone cases can be found in upland burns; one of these *A. fuscipes* has been noted from a Raasay burn and from the Kinloch river on Rhum where it is stated to be locally abundant. Lochs are more productive of beetles and water bugs but the water cricket *Velia caprai* is common in streams devoid of vegetation and on an Islay burn I have seen numbers in the basin at the foot of a waterfall. The moorland pondskater *Gerris costai* normally inhabits pools but it has been recorded from a Benbecula stream. Of the lesser water boatmen *Hesperocorixa castanea* is stated by Dr G. A. Walton to be the second most abundant species in the Hebrides and occurs in slow-moving streams as well as bog pools. The slower-flowing streams have their quota of water beetles and twenty species have been recorded from Islay rivers although the adjoining island of Jura has only nine.

Flatworms are present in the streams under stones or on the underside of the leaves of aquatic plants and a glacial relict of this group, *Planaria alpina*, has been noted from a spring on Canna and may well occur elsewhere in the region. Under stones in the small streams of this island a common flatworm found is *Polycelis cornuta*, a species whose habitat requirements, unlike some others of its kind, demand a swift clear current. There is another class of flatworms known as the Trematodes which are popularly called 'flukes' some of which have quite complicated parasitical life histories. One such is the sheep liver fluke. The eggs of this flatworm pass out on to grass in the sheep's excreta and when the temperature is right they develop into first-stage larvae which seek out one particular kind of snail, the dwarf pond snail *Limnaea truncatula*; they penetrate these and inside the snail's body undergo a mysterious change into a different kind of larvae. These have tadpole-like tails and they emerge and swim around in the marshy meadows which are the home of the snail. Eventually some of them are eaten by sheep and move to the liver where they are the cause of a serious disease in the animal. Human beings can sometimes be infected if they eat unwashed, wild watercress. Certain areas of Britain are more infested with this obnoxious parasite than others and parts at least of the Hebridean region, Coll and Muck for example, are so affected.

The freshwater shrimp *Gammarus pulex* is a characteristic in-habitant of shallow rivers but on Barra a brackish water species *G. duebeni* has taken the place of *pulex* perhaps because on this exposed island there is sufficient salt spray carried by the winds to provide a satisfactory environment. Conversely, the salt atmosphere of the smaller islands has an adverse effect on the freshwater snails for many species cannot tolerate salt; in conse-quence the molluscan community of the burns is an impoverished one. Two species, the wandering snail *Limnaea pereger* and the river limpet *Ancylus fluviatilis* will accept saline conditions and they are common on some islands. Dr Charles Elton found not only the wandering snail in a burn on Pabbay in the Sound of Harris but also the round-spired trumpet snail *Planorbis spirorbis* which although a common species in Britain generally was the first record for the Hebrides. River mussels *Unio margaritifer* are reported from Jura and probably occur on other islands.

The coarse fisherman will not make his way to the Western Isles but the rivers and burns have their quota of brown trout and some have, in lesser numbers, sea trout. The region as a whole is not noted for large numbers of salmon but Skye, North Uist, Harris and Lewis are renowned for their salmon fishing and the Grimersta river and loch complex in Lewis has been called the finest salmon water in Europe. Eels travel along the burns and the little three-spined sticklebacks can be seen.

Most of the rivers are too small to attract much in the way of birdlife. Wagtails and water belong together and pied and grey wagtails frequent the streams of the Inner Isles; the pied is a scarce nester in the Outer Isles but the grey does not breed there. The yellow wagtail is occasionally seen on migration even as far west as St Kilda. The white wagtail is a passage migrant in both groups of islands and in 1972 mixed pairs of white and pied were reported nesting on Islay. On this island the kingfisher has been recorded breeding on the Laggan river. Another small-time predator is the dipper which feeds mainly on aquatic insects; as noted in Chapter One most of the population belongs to the Irish race. A familiar sound along the streams in summer is the piping of the common sandpiper; it is not as numerous as on the mainland but appears to be common enough especially on Harris and Lewis. The heron's interest in the rivers is solely in the fish they contain and it nests elsewhere. Reed buntings and sedge warblers are the two small birds of reed swamp and both appear to be on the increase in recent years.

Mammalian life is represented by only three species and a casual observer would be fortunate indeed to see any of them. Otters are the most numerous and widespread but are mainly nocturnal of habit and elusive although their whistling call may be heard on a summer evening. The little water shrew is extremely scarce but they have been recorded in recent years on Skye, Mull, Raasay and Garbh Eileach in the Isles of the Sea. In the 1960s feral mink became established over a wide area of southern, central and western Lewis. They are not restricted to rivers but since their principal food is fish they spend much time along the rivers and lochs.

LOCHS

Most of the islands are well-endowed with lochs; it has been estimated that Lewis alone possesses a thousand. Anyone standing on South Lee in North Uist and surveying the complex of lochs to westward might well think that the island had more fresh water than dry land. The area of North Uist lochs totals no less than 8,000 acres (3,240 hectares). Some have extraordinarily irregular outlines; one such is Loch Scadavay on North Uist which although its dimensions are only about two miles (3·2km) by four miles (6·4km) has a perimeter of fifty miles (80·5km). It is not only their outlines which are complicated but also the hollows which they occupy. For example, Loch Langavat on Lewis covers no less than eight separate rock basins. Lochs vary from the glacially eroded basin of Loch Coruisk in the Cuillins of Skye to little boggy moorland pools and the alkaline machair lochs a few feet above sea level. Depths range from the few inches of a peaty lochan to the 219ft (66·7m) of Loch Suainaval in western Lewis.

A specialised flora grows in the lochs and includes some rarities. Emergent vegetation on the margins often consist of the common reed, water horsetail and bottle sedge *Carex rostrata*. The fen sedge *Cladium mariscus* is plentiful on the shore of a loch on South Rona and grows on several other islands. On stony bottoms in shallow water the submerged plants shoreweed *Littorella uniflora* and water lobelia *Lobelia dortmanna* are plentiful and the awlwort *Subularia aquatica* is fairly common in some lochs. A very local species, waterwort *Elatine hexandra*, grows in shallow water on peat in Loch St Clair on Barra and in one or two other places in the Outer Isles. The pillwort *Pilularia globulifera* is a strange little plant, a water fern which grows on the margins of lochs. It derives its name from the small, round, spore-bearing capsules situated on the creeping rootstock; it is present in varying frequency in the region. Also growing in this marginal habitat is a speciality of the Hebrides whose phytogeographical importance has been referred to in Chapter One. This is the pipewort *Eriocaulon septangulare* located either on wet ground adjoining lochs or in the water with the lead-coloured flowers projecting above the surface during late summer. The erect, twisted stem provides the origin of the colloquial name for when the pith was removed this stem was supposed to have served as a pipe. The plant is known in the Hebrides only from Coll, Skye and Scalpay but on the first named island it occurs in abundance on certain of the lochs.

Growing on the loch bottoms farther out in the water is another strange plant which is neither a wild flower nor a true fern. This is the quillwort *Isoetes lacustris* of wide distribution though not very numerous. Four islands, Islay, Colonsay, South and North Uist have another very local, submerged aquatic, the flexible or slender naiad *Najas flexilis*. This is a true flowering plant with grass-like leaves. It is reported to be plentiful in Loch Grogary on North Uist and occurs in a number of lochs in the mid-western part of South Uist. Much more common submerged plants are the milfoils *Myriophyllum spicatum* and *M. alterniflorum*. The latter tends to have a north-western distribution with a preference for acid water and over the islands as a whole is the dominant species but the former is recorded as the commonest species in Barra, Coll, Tiree and Gunna.

The floating plants of this zone are the water lilies and pondweeds. The yellow water lily *Nuphar lutea* adds a splash of colour to a few lochs; it is very uncommon in the islands but it has been recorded from Mull, Scalpay, Lismore, Skye, North Uist and Harris. The white water lily *Nymphaea alba* is much more widespread and quite common on a number of islands. The small form, *N. a. occidentalis* is of scattered occurrence and is probably more common in the Outer Isles. Pondweeds flourish in considerable variety and have been studied in some detail; some seventeen out of the twenty-one British species of this genus have been found in the region. Professor H. Harrison noted a definite linking of the species distribution with the pH value of the water, the alkaline machair lochs having the greatest number of species. Many Hebridean lochs are situated on acid moorland and here two typical species are the floating or broad-leaved pondweed *Potamogeton natans* and bog pondweed *P. polygonifolius*. Neither is confined to moorland lochs but the latter has a preference for them. Taking the country as a whole it is probably true to say that the floating pondweed is the commonest species but in the Hebrides it takes second place to the bog pondweed. A number of rare species and hybrids occur and in some lochs the cover of pondweed may be so dense as to cause a problem to anglers. Bur-reed *Sparganium* spp are generally uncommon in the islands but these emergent plants are sometimes present in this zone of deeper water. In Skye and Rhum it is mainly the floating bur-reed *S. angustifolium* but in many lochs on Coll and Tiree the species present is the red-stemmed variety of the branched bur-reed *S. erectum* var *neglectum* which is of very local distribution in Britain.

The small peaty pools have a rather different flora dominated by plants of bogs and marshes. Bogbean *Menyanthes trifoliata*, lesser bladderwort *Utricularia minor*, lesser spearwort *Ranunculus flammula* and common spike rush *Eleocharis palustris* are some of them. Very different in character from either these boggy pools or the large acid lochs are the strongly alkaline lochs on the limestone island of Lismore where the water is so impregnated with lime that the pebbles on the shores are lime-encrusted and the clarity is such that the bottom can be seen through 25ft (7·6m) of water. On the surface is lime-loving plankton; carpeting the bottom is a dense cover of those primitive plants the stoneworts. Between them, submerged in the water are plants of water milfoil so heavily encrusted with lime deposits that they cannot surface in order to flower. Floating plants are represented by yellow water lily and various pondweeds whilst emergent vegetation includes water plantain *Alisma plantago-aquatica* and mare's tail *Hippuris vulgaris*. There is clearly much of interest to the dedicated botanist in Hebridean lochs but lacking thigh boots, boats and specialised equipment the casual visitor will have to content himself with an aesthetic appreciation of the scene. Gazing on the giant white cups of the water lilies resting on their even larger green saucers on a hot summer's day it is easy for one to understand the languor-inducing magic of the lotus fable but here in the abrasive, astringent Hebrides the antidote is ready to hand in the wind forever rustling through the reeds and the perpetual motion of the water's surface. For many, this visual enjoyment will be satisfaction enough.

The invertebrate life of the lochs is fairly considerable and contains some northern elements. In the micro-lepidoptera there is one small family of aquatic insects, often called the china mark moths. The caterpillars have an unusual life history; they hatch out below water and have a mainly aquatic existence. In their early stages they feed on the stems of water plants later floating to the surface to feed on the leaves of pondweeds and water lilies. Here they protect themselves by building a case of leaf fragments in the manner of caddis fly larvae to which they bear some resemblance and later descend once more to the loch bottom to hibernate. Some vegetarian species of caddis flies feed with them on the leaves of these plants. A northern species *Philopotamus montanus* usually inhabiting mountain streams has been noted in abundance in one small loch on Raasay. Loch St Clair on Barra provides a favourable habitat and no less than fifteen species of caddis flies have been recorded here.

The water bugs of the Hebrides have been studied by Dr G. A. Walton and others. The most interesting fact in general about this large group is that unlike so many other Hebridean animals they have not evolved into the characteristic dark island forms. Dr Walton suggests that this is because they are an ancient group able to a considerable extent to resist the prevalent evolutionary influences. Some genera are scarce but the lesser water boatmen, the Corixids, are not only numerous but also exceptionally rich in species; some forty or so are known to occur which is about half the British total and quite remarkable bearing in mind that island isolation normally means an impoverished fauna. It has been suggested that the cool summer temperature is probably the determinative factor in the case of many species.

Five out of seven of the British species of pondskater occur but they are not plentiful. These are the insects with long legs which skim over the water surface in small parties. There are some differences in the distributional pattern compared with that of the mainland. The most widespread and commonest British pondskater is *Gerris lacustris* but in the Hebrides it is known only from the southern part of the Inner Isles where it has been recorded from Islay, Jura and Ulva. The moorland pondskater *G. costai* is the northern insect which replaces it and which is well distributed throughout most of the islands; a frequent habitat is peaty pools such as those formed by peat cuttings but it has been observed even in brackish water where also may be found *G. thoracicus*, another species able to tolerate saline conditions although it lives in ditches and silty ponds as well; it has a rather scattered and local distribution in the region. The water scorpion *Nepa cinerea* is quite scarce but has been noted from Islay, Canna, Barra and the brackish water lochs of North Uist. In most habitats throughout Britain the common water boatman *Notonecta glauca* is the dominant species of the genus and although uncommon in the Hebrides it is known from several of the islands including South Rona and Barra where it has been identified from a number of lochs. In the main, however, it is replaced in the Hebrides by *N. obliqua*, the typical species of acid northern pools.

The rich variety of lesser water boatman has already been mentioned. There are several ubiquitous species. The most numerous of these is *Sigara scotti*, the specific name deriving not from Scotland but from an entomologist who specialised in the study of water bugs. This is an insect with a preference for acid peaty lochs with fairly sparse vegetation. The second commonest lesser water boatman is *Hesperocorixa castanea* which is especially associated with *Sphagnum* moss and generally lives in pools and lochs where the organic content is higher than those inhabited by *Sigara scotti*. At least four other species are found almost everywhere. The least favoured habitat is the large deep loch with stony bottom which carries few if any Corixids at all. Two boreo-alpine relict species are *Glaenocorisa propinqua* and *Arctocoriza carinata* found in acid moorland pools.

The Hebridean lochs also hold a varied and interesting assemblage of water beetles. The large lochs may not have any beetles at all and the best kind are the smaller lochs with clear water and varied vegetation. Ninety-three spp have been recorded from the Western Isles generally and the majority live in the lochs. Three of them are not known in any other region of Britain and derive from the Mediterranean area. The sensational discoveries of these three have been described in Chapter One. Also referred to in that chapter are four boreal or alpine relict species, *Dytiscus lapponicus*, *Agabus arcticus*, *Deronectes assimilis* and *Gyrinus opacus*. The first named is the largest of the four although the smallest of its own genus, about 25mm in length, and it has a scattered but local distribution in both island groups; on the mainland this insect lives chiefly in mountain lochans but on Raasay where it is widespread it is found in low-level lochs. *Agabus arcticus* is a medium-sized beetle which together with the surface-dwelling whirligig beetle *Gyrinus opacus* may have survived the last glaciation. There is considerable variety and the commonest species on one island may not be the commonest on the adjacent one; for example, the little *Hydroporus palustris* has been noted as the dominant water beetle in the lochs of Islay while on the adjoining island of Jura its place is taken by *Agabus arcticus* and *A. bipustulatus*. Some beetles are very localised, occurring on one or two islands but scarce or absent elsewhere in the Hebrides for example *Laccobius nigriceps* which is present only on Barra and *Haliplus ruficollis* which is fairly numerous on Barra and Tiree but very scarce on the other isles. There still remains scope for distributional studies and as recently as 1970 five spp of water beetles were added to the St Kilda list.

There is an impoverished dragonfly fauna in the Western Isles compared with England, three-quarters of the British species being absent. The golden-ringed has already been mentioned. The blue aeshna *Aeshna caerulea* is a northern insect, rare in Britain, but nymphs of this dragonfly have been noted in lochans on Rhum. The only other large hawker dragonfly occurring is the common aeshna *A. juncea* the nymphs of which live in peat pools. It flies in late summer and autumn. There are a few of the medium-sized darter dragonflies. The black-legged sub-species of the common sympetrum *Sympetrum striolatum nigrifemur* is probably the commonest of these. The black sympetrum *S. danae* is one of the few dragonflies which is more common and widespread in Scotland than elsewhere in Britain and it is well distributed in the islands. The four-spotted Libellula *Libellula quadrimaculata* is locally common and in contrast to the preceding three, is a spring-flying dragonfly. The nymph of the keeled orthetrum *Orthetrum coerulescens* lives in boggy streams and pools; it is very scarce in the region but possibly rather more common than the records suggest. Four damsel flies have been recorded, large red *Pyrrhosoma nymphula*, common ischnura *Ischnura elegans*, common blue *Enallagma cyathigerum* and common coenagrion *Coenagrion puella*. The last named may only breed on Skye. The Outer Isles provide very exposed conditions for dragonflies and fewer species are present.

As might be expected, the richest areas for freshwater snails are the alkaline lochs and notable in this respect are the limestone lochs of Lismore where a total of fourteen spp have been recorded. The most numerous of these snails is the keeled trumpet snail *Planorbis carinatus* var *dubia* and it is interesting to note that this is the north-east Ireland form, yet one more link in the chain of evidence connecting Ireland with the Hebrides. The second most abundant species on Lismore is the wandering snail *Limnaea pereger* which over Britain as a whole is the commonest freshwater snail. Another member of this genus on Lismore is the giant pond snail *L. stagnalis* which is nearly twice the size of the wandering snail and although widespread in England is very scarce in Scotland. Wherever on other islands there are lochs which are rich in nutrients there will be freshwater snails. One of the most widespread is the river limpet which can be found on the margins of lochs as well as rivers and occurs on even the small sub-oceanic islands because of its ability to tolerate salt. One such nutrient-rich loch is Loch Cill Chriosd on Skye which in addition to the wandering snail and river limpet has the white trumpet snail *Planorbis albus* and a tiny pea-shell cockle *Pisidium nitidum*. The Barra lochs have several species of these minute cockles but they are so small and so similar that they can only be identified by experienced conchologists. Just as the river limpet is not restricted to moving water so the river sponge *Ephydatia fluviatilis* occurs also in some of the lochs. The discovery of an Irish–American sponge in the lochs of Barra has been referred to in Chapter One.

The brackish water lochs that are found in several places in the Outer Hebrides but particularly on North Uist deserve a mention on their own for their unusual floral and faunal assemblage, a combination of marine and freshwater plants and animals. The more seaward of these waters have an extensive growth of seaweeds, wracks, tangleweeds and some red algae but they also have a characteristic brackish water flowering plant, the beaked tassel pondweed *Ruppia maritima*. Here at the outlet to the sea there is a rich marine fauna of sea-anemones, starfish, periwinkles and bristle worms. Amongst the floating fronds of the seaweeds there are other marine animals including a spire shell *Hydrobia ventrosa* and the shrimp *Gammarus duebeni* which are always associated with brackish conditions. Farther inland there is a markedly freshwater character to the aquatic flora with milfoil, water lobelia and bur-reed but living amongst them are animals typical of estuarine conditions; in addition to *G. duebeni* there are three-spined sticklebacks, flounders and Jenkin's spire shell. These intermingle with nymphs of dragonflies, pondskaters and other insects of freshwater. The most extraordinary aspect is that mentioned by Martin Martin as long ago as 1695 that these lochs had cod, ling and mackerel in them. To a lesser degree certain brackish lochs of Barra have a somewhat similar admixture of species.

The fish of the rivers find their way into the lochs. Brown trout are abundant but sea trout and salmon much less so. A small red-coloured variety of trout lives in Loch Frisa in the north of Mull. Sticklebacks can be seen in the amazingly clear water of the Lismore lochs. The char is a beautifully coloured fish belonging to the salmon family which is found in some Hebridean lochs including Loch Fada on North Uist and some lochs on Raasay. There is no doubt that it is an arctic relict species which became cut off in northern Britain in isolated communities during the Pleistocene period and as a consequence has developed into separate races.

Knowledge of the pattern of bird distribution in the Western Isles is not as complete as one might expect especially as regards the winter visitors. Many of the islands are still relatively isolated, comparatively few of the islanders are knowledgeable about birds particularly on the smaller islands and the bird populations themselves are subject to erratic fluctuations. In many instances, therefore, it is not possible to give detailed information of distribution. Herons wade in the shallows and round the loch shores a familiar sound in summer is the piping of the common sandpiper. The former bird is fairly widespread throughout both island groups although it did not arrive in the Outer Isles until the present century. There is not a great deal of scope in the islands for the traditional nesting site at the top of tall trees and a variety of sites are utilised, ranging through reed beds, heather, cliff ledges and scrub. A favourite situation is in the scrub growth on loch islets a notable example of this being on the islands in Loch Druidibeg on South Uist where a long-established heronry amongst the rhododendrons has been in existence since 1922.

Gulleries of the black-headed gull are sometimes sited on loch islands and I recall a colourful and animated scene on Loch Sandary on North Uist where tightly packed gulls were nesting on an islet amongst a golden mass of marsh marigold. This appears to be one of the birds which breeds more prolifically in the Outer than in the Inner Isles. Loch islands are also a favourite nesting site of common gulls which are more widespread and numerous than the preceding species. That common bird of farm and village ponds, the moorhen, is scarce and localised; this may seem surprising in view of the large amount of freshwater sites available but muddy ponds and peaty lochans are two different habitats and water birds in general are not very adaptable. The status of the coot is somewhat similar although in the Outer Hebrides it is fairly common in the nutrient-rich machair lochs of the Uists. The little grebe appears to be more plentiful perhaps because it will accept a rather wider range of habitat; it is reported very scarce on Islay but it certainly occurs and I have seen it on Loch Ballygrant; although it does not nest in all the islands it is well distributed and is particularly common in the Uists. The red-throated diver breeds on many of the islands both in small lochans and the larger lochs and it is especially characteristic of moorland waters. This is a species whose breeding success is closely dependent on optimal weather conditions and a relatively slight change of water level may be disastrous owing to the nest site being so often at or near the water's edge. Its close relative the black-throated diver is much scarcer nesting in small numbers on Mull, Skye, Harris and Lewis.

Mute swans are irregularly distributed but generally are restricted in the breeding season to the central and southern parts of both island groups, not usually nesting north of Tiree in the Inner Isles or North Uist in the Outer Isles. I have found them exceptionally numerous in North Uist but one of the largest breeding colonies is on Loch Bee in the northern part of South Uist where up to 300 pairs may nest. A study is being made of communication in this species on the Uists, in particular amongst the birds on this loch. Whooper swans will sometimes stay well on into the summer; I have seen them on Loch Hallan on South Uist and Loch Scolpaig on North Uist at the end of May. The only wild goose regularly present and breeding in the summer is the greylag; wild birds nest in South Uist, Benbecula and North Uist and a feral population lives on Coll. The main breeding centre of the wild stock is at Loch Druidibeg on South Uist where some seventy pairs now nest. The population was fairly constant at about thirty pairs for twenty years after World War II but it then increased rapidly to its present size and crofters have become concerned about damage to their crops. A five year study by Dr I. Newton has shown that a determining factor in breeding success is the condition of the grass. For long the significance of this loch as a focal point for the recolonising of the Hebrides has been recognised but the problem is how this can be effected without an excessive colony developing at least temporarily to the detriment of the crofters' livelihood. Feral Canada geese breed on Colonsay.

Mallard are the commonest nesting duck but a number of other species breed with varying degrees of regularity. Both island groups have teal, tufted, wigeon, gadwall and shoveller though by no means on every island; the only nesting duck on the Small Isles' freshwater lochs, for example, is mallard. The status of the common scoter seems decidedly obscure but it is believed to be at least an occasional nester on Islay. Pochard and pintail breed irregularly in the Outer Hebrides. Red-breasted mergansers are more typical of sea lochs but they do also frequent freshwater and are widespread in the islands.

The outstanding speciality of Hebridean lochs remains to be mentioned. It is the red-necked phalarope, that small and elegant wader which has never been numerous but is now extremely scarce. Its preferred habitat is small lochans especially the machair lochs of the Outer Isles. A boreal species, the phalarope is circumpolar in its breeding range. They are extraordinary little creatures in more than one way. They are extremely tame not only in their breeding haunts but also out of the nesting season. A curious, characteristic habit of spinning round in the water is probably a method of disturbing invertebrate prey. Another strange aspect of the phalarope's behaviour pattern is the change of role in the sexes in that like the dotterel, the male bird does all the incubation and the female bears the brightest plumage. They tend to nest in small colonies if the population density permits.

The advent of winter sees a change in the wildfowl populations. Many of the breeding greylag in the Uists move off from their nesting areas and their place is taken by others of their kind from farther north together with barnacle, white-fronted and pink-footed geese. Barnacle geese are the most handsome of all the British geese and these fine birds are becoming increasingly numerous in the Hebrides in the wintertime occurring throughout both island groups not only on the large islands but also on small ones like the Treshnish Isles and even on islets such as Eilean nan Ron, near Oronsay. By far the largest wintering flocks, however, are to be found on Islay where numbers have increased in recent years from 10,000 to the fantastic total of 17,000. These flocks when on the wing have been reckoned as

one of the spectacular sights of the Hebrides and certainly I count
the sight one of my great birding experiences. Taking the
islands as a whole they must hold in winter no less than a third
of the total world population of barnacle geese. The chief
Scottish wintering haunts of the Greenland race of the white-
fronted goose are the Hebrides. Although the numbers are not
as great as those of barnacle it is probable that the proportion of
the world population is the same and it is similarly widespread.
The largest number probably also winter on Islay where the
population may reach up to 4,000. Rodney Dawson who farms
on the island points out that there is limited competition between the two species because the whitefront's preference is for
rough, marshy fields such as may be found on the desolate Oa
peninsula and parts of the Rhinns. They can sometimes, however, be seen feeding in the same pasture as barnacles. In smaller
numbers greylags have a scattered distribution from Islay to
Harris. Pink-feet are scarce winter visitors but are seen more
plentifully as passage migrants and odd birds have summered in
one or two places such as at the Butt of Lewis and on Coll in
recent years. Brent geese are even scarcer but an occasional bird
of the pale-breasted race turns up here and there. The numbers
of whooper swans vary from year to year and Loch Bee on
South Uist is a favourite haunt. The breeding ducks are augmented by winter immigrants, mallard, wigeon, pochard, tufted
and golden-eye.

Amphibians have a curiously restricted distribution. None are
found in the Outer Isles and in the Inner Isles newts are localised
in a handful of islands; Skye and Rhum have both smooth and
palmate newts, Tiree has only the smooth but Mull and Scarba
only the palmate; the crested newt does not occur. It is possible
that the first two may yet be found on other islands. Frogs and
toads are well distributed in the Inner Hebrides although the
former are stated to be very scarce on Jura. There are only two
aquatic mammals, the indigenous otter and, on Lewis, the
alien mink.

H

CHAPTER SIX

Woodlands

Vegetation—Invertebrate life—Birds—Mammals

VEGETATION

SOMEONE WHO HAS MADE a quick and casual visit to a few of the smaller islands may be inclined to enquire, with a trace of scorn, as to the whereabouts of any wood. Dr Johnson when on Mull made a characteristically mordant remark exclaiming to his host that he mistook a wood for a heath. Without in the least excusing his impoliteness to his hospitable companion one can see his point. To a man accustomed to the dense forests of England or even the well-wooded policies of southern Scotland, the term 'wood' seems somewhat of an exaggeration for much which passes for it in the Scottish islands. It takes but little reflection, however, to realise that it is quite unreasonable to expect to find much in the way of well-developed deciduous forest in these conditions of extreme exposure. In an entirely different way Hebridean arboriculture can hold as much of interest as that of the mainland. Such interest lies in tracing the varying fortunes of the trees from prehistoric times, the study of relict woodland which survives in sheltered spots, the detecting of former woods in areas where now the herb layer alone exists and in the forester's tactical battles against the wind and salt spray as he selects and plants, partly by a process of trial and error, various trees in experimental plots.

If areas of thick deciduous forest would seem unbelievable in many parts of the Hebrides today it has not always been so. The glaciers of the Ice Age had not long departed before tiny seed-

lings of birch and pine began appearing amongst the arctic
vegetation. With the coming of the Boreal period perhaps
10,000 years ago hazel became much more prominent. Then
3,000 years later the climate, whilst still retaining summer
warmth, became much wetter; this, the Atlantic period, was the
time when woodlands covered very extensive areas of the
Western Isles more especially on the lower ground and in the
eastern part of the islands. Oak and alder became components of
the forest although it is unlikely that they luxuriated to the same
extent as on the mainland. For the next 2,000 years the forests of
the Hebrides were at their peak although their fortunes have
waxed and waned several times since then.

The direct evidence for the existence of these forests is provided in two ways; the first by analysis and dating of the pollen
grains in the peat and the second by the remains of forests in
bogs and in a number of places along the western shore of the
Long Island. Dr Charles Elton records a buried hazel wood on
Pabbay in the Sound of Harris, an island which is now completely treeless. A number of factors contributed to the virtual
disappearance of woodland. There is a strong tradition in Lewis
that Norsemen destroyed the tree cover there. More likely
reasons were changes in sea level, coastal erosion, clearance for
sheep, the need for timber and the development of strong
westerly winds. Natural woodland still grew in varying quantities on Mull, Rhum, Skye and other islands in the seventeenth
century but in the following century destruction was almost
complete except for the small relict patches to which we now
turn.

The fragments of natural woodland that remain are found in
several different situations on cliffs, islands on lochs, valleys and
ravines. The shrubs of coastal cliffs have already been referred to
in Chapter Three but it should be noted that they are to be
found also on inland cliffs. The cliffs of Rhum have stunted
hazel and a little sessile oak but neither are common; a few
degenerate hazels are recorded from North Harris and there are
areas of hazel scrub in several of the Inner Hebrides. The most

outstanding examples of wooded loch islets that I have seen are those on Loch Druidibeg in South Uist where dense coverts of rhododendron grow; these of course are not native but rowan *Sorbus aucuparia*, birch *Betula pubescens*, common sallow *Salix cineraria* and juniper *Juniperus communis* are also present and these are certainly relics of former more extensive woodland. The most notable area of natural scrub along streamsides in the Outer Isles is also on South Uist, on the banks of the Allt Volagir which drains the southern slopes of Beinn Mhor. Here grows a community of aspen–hazel–birch scrub which has been studied by ecologists. Aspens are widespread in the Outer Hebrides; they grow on cliffs on the eastern side of Mingulay and Benbecula and are reported to be numerous in gorges on Barra. They are equally well distributed in the Inner Isles. Scarba, the small island north of Jura has small natural oak woods with sallow and birch. Gullies on the island of Soay off south-west Skye hold birch, rowan, several species of willow and one or two trees of sessile oak which although extremely scarce in the region are nevertheless of interest in that they indicate the existence of oak woodland in the past. Further confirmation of this has been provided on Soay by borings. The island is divided into two parts by a narrow isthmus and borings into the mud produced much oak and alder pollen mixed with marine diatoms; this invasion of the sea probably took place during the Atlantic period about 5,000–7,000 years ago when Soay would have been two islands. Alder is not uncommon along the wetter margins of river valleys and drier niches have rowan.

Certain areas of limestone have a rich and distinctive arboreal flora. The Isles of the Sea in the Firth of Lorne have some Dalradian limestone which in the glens carries a dense and varied scrub. This is composed of birch, rowan, hazel, hawthorn, alder and a natural hybrid of the common sallow and eared willow which is the dominant shrub. The largest island, Garbh Eileach, has a wood which contains ash, that typical tree of calcareous soils. The peninsula of Sleat in the southern part of Skye has a small area of Cambrian limestone and on this

rock there is an ash wood at Tokavaig. An associated tree here is
the bird cherry *Prunus padus*. The island of Lismore is a mass of
Dalradian limestone and up to the seventeenth century was well-
wooded; today there are still isolated ash trees growing on the
limestone but the woods have gone.

Indirect evidence for the greater extent of Hebridean woodland in former times can also be adduced by the localities where
the trees have gone but a relict herb layer remains. Some of these
sites have been mentioned already in Chapter Three but other
examples can be quoted. In some gorges on Rhum where no
trees now remain there are bluebells *Endymion non-scriptus*, wood
sorrel *Oxalis acetosella*, wood vetch *Vicia sylvatica*, wood sanicle
Sanicula europaea, wood sage *Teucrium scorodonia*, ransoms *Allium
ursinum* and wood horsetail *Equisetum sylvaticum*. The island of
Scarp off the western coast of Harris has a similar though more
restricted woodland flora and it has been suggested that these
are remains of woods which existed in the warm, dry climate of
sub-Boreal times which followed the Atlantic period 4,000 years
ago.

Despite the great reduction in wooded areas, where conditions
are favourable trees will still spread. M. J. Delaney and W. O.
Copland in a survey in 1958 of South Rona noted that after the
depopulation of the island in 1943 (apart from the lighthouse
keepers) patches of scrub had developed and existing small woods
had increased in area.

The woods of the present day can be placed in three categories,
the relict woodlands, the private plantings chiefly around the
great houses such as Stornoway Castle on Lewis, Kinloch Castle
on Rhum, Raasay House on Raasay, and Dunvegan Castle on
Skye, and thirdly the gradually increasing Forestry Commission plantations. The largest proportion of woods are sited
on the eastern side of the islands although there are a few notable
exceptions. The amenity plantings in the vicinity of the large
houses have relatively large oak, ash, beech and sycamore.
Many of these mature woods are very attractive in appearance;
some, such as the Stornoway and Raasay woods, have dense

thickets of rhododendrons which make a spectacular sight in
May. The trees at Dunvegan are festooned with leafy lichens
and carpeted with ferns and many of the trees in Stornoway
woods are draped with *Usnea* lichens, a sure indication of the
purity of the air. Beautiful, too, are the Ballygrant woods on
Islay where beech, oak, horse chestnut and a variety of ornamental conifers are underplanted with rhododendrons and the
whole encircles the still waters of Loch Ballygrant. Barra has
three woods which though small in extent have a considerable
variety of mainly deciduous trees. Surprising for such a wind-
swept isle one of these species is the sweet chestnut, a tree of the
warm south. The strawberry trees *Arbutus unedo* on Scarba have
almost certainly been planted. Apart from amenity plantings of
specimen ornamental conifers, private plantations have been
made such as that of Corsican pine on Canna in 1911, of mountain pine at Borve on Harris and of mixed conifers on Muck in
1922. The third type of wood is that planted by the Forestry
Commission and the area of their plantations exceeds the other
two categories combined although planting did not begin until
1924. They are the largest landowners in Mull with just over
14,000 acres planted. The predominant conifers in these Mull
plantations are Sitka spruce with much smaller numbers of
Japanese larch. The only trees that Tiree has possessed have been
one or two stunted specimens round a few of the crofts but
recently a tiny experimental plot has been planted near Scarinish
to see which type, if any, can survive on such a gale-prone
island. The proportion of land under afforestation of the total
area of the Hebrides is very small but the steady increase of
woodland should begin to enlarge the variety of wildlife and this,
in fact, is already happening.

The natural woodland has a rich ground layer of mosses, as
is to be expected in the moist atmosphere of western Britain.
Common species include *Hypnum cupressiforme*, *H. schreberi*,
Mnium hornum and *Eurrhynchium praelonga* amongst a number of
others; in one of the Barra woods branches are clothed with an
epiphytic moss *Ulota phyllantha*. There is perhaps not the variety

of fungi of mainland woods but some such as *Boletus, Russula, Lactarius,* and *Mycena* species are evident in the autumn; old birches have their quota of bracket fungi and the delightfully apricot-scented chanterelle *Cantharellus cibarius* has been recorded from Portree wood on Skye and no doubt is present in other woods as well.

The flowers of the semi-natural woodlands and the ornamental deciduous ones are those of open woods anywhere in Britain. In both island groups there are primroses, violets, bluebells, foxgloves, herb Robert and wood sorrel. Raasay woods have a rich flora which includes early purple orchid, wood sanicle, wood ruff and pignut. The introduced pink-flowered North American plant *Montia sibirica* is recorded as abundant in the Raasay House woods and the Cornish moneywort *Sibthorpia europaea* has been introduced to Stornoway Woods. The sword-leaved helleborine *Cephalanthum longifolia* grows in the Armadale woods on Skye, its only station in the Hebrides. Enchanter's nightshade *Circaea lutetiana* is scarce but occurs on Scalpay, Eigg and the Sleat district of Skye. In the more exposed Outer Isles only seven species of wild flowers are present in the Barra woods.

Young coniferous plantations still retain the flowers of the heathland such as tormentil *Potentilla erecta* and heath bedstraw *Gallium saxatile*. In the shadier parts of the woods ferns are plentiful; hard fern *Blechnum spicant* and male fern *Dryopteris filix-mas* are generally the two dominant species but lady fern *Athyrium filix-femina*, Wilson's filmy fern *Hymenophyllum wilsonii*, hart's tongue *Phyllites scolopendrium* and species of buckler ferns are often present. In the section of the Mull Forest between Salen and Tobermory there is an extremely rich bryophytic flora and even the dead branches on the ground are completely covered with green moss. The shrubs usually occurring are species of rose, bramble *Rubus fruticosus* and the Hebridean form of the honeysuckle *Lonicera periclymenum* var *clarkii*.

INVERTEBRATE LIFE

If wooded areas are scarce in the Hebrides so also are many of the insects which one would expect to see inhabiting them. The lepidopterist, for example, will find but few butterflies. Flying in the woods of Jura, northern Mull, Ulva, Rhum, Soay and Skye, however, is an island race of the small pearl-bordered fritillary *Boloria selene insularum* which is more brightly coloured than the type. The pearl-bordered fritillary *B. euphrosyne* is virtually unknown in the region but it has been recorded from Rhum. The speckled wood *Pararge aegeria* is at the northern limits of its range in Britain but can be found on Islay, Mull, Ulva, Eigg, Rhum and Skye. Another typical butterfly of mainland woodland glades, the ringlet *Aphantopus hyperantus* has been recorded only from the woods of Colonsay. The Scotch argus *Erebia aethiops* is most often found in moist spots in open country but it has penetrated into some of the woods of Mull. The green-veined white *Pieris napi* is another butterfly of damp, open sites which is, however, fairly common in the early stages of coniferous plantings on the open moor and in open woods. The green hairstreak *Callophrys rubi* flies on the Rhinns of Islay, Rhum and Canna.

The semi-natural woods of aspen and sallow on Colonsay, Mull, Rhum and Canna provide food for the caterpillars of the large and conspicuous poplar hawk moth *Laothoe populi*. The poplar lutestring *Tethea or* is another common moth associated with aspen on which the caterpillars feed. The swallow prominent *Pheosia tremula* is found on Eigg, Mull and Colonsay where aspen is probably the main food plant of the larvae although willow is occasionally eaten. The reverse situation exists with the pebble prominent *Eligmodonta ziczac* with willow the preferred food; this moth is recorded from Canna, Rhum, Skye and Colonsay. The larvae of the well known puss moth *Cerura vinula* devour leaves of either genus with impartiality and this moth is widespread; it is one of several kinds of moths which have caused serious damage to young trees on Rhum. The caterpillars of the May highflyer *Hydriomena coerulata* can be seen on alder leaves in the Stornoway woods and these same trees also harbour the larvae of the iron prominent *Notodonta dromedarius* which occurs also on Skye, Soay, Canna, Rhum and Colonsay. Unlike the May highflyer they are not confined to alder but feed sometimes on birch and hazel.

A number of moths are specifically associated with birch. The yellow horned *Achlya flavicornis* is flying around the bursting leaf buds in the Hebridean spring on Colonsay, Mull, Canna and Rhum. A little later the lesser swallow prominent *Pheosia gnoma* emerges on Mull, Rhum, Canna and Soay, the scalloped hook-tip *Drepana lacertinaria* is resting on birch twigs on Mull and the birch mocha *Cosymbia pendularia* so drab of appearance, is making its insignificant flights in the birch woods of Raasay. Full summer sees the advent of the common lutestring *Ochropacha duplaris* on Mull, Rhum, Skye and Raasay.

The clumps of juniper have their own distinctive fauna. The chestnut-coloured carpet moth *Thera cognata* is plentiful on Iona and on Canna where the juniper pug *Eupithecia pusillata* is also located. The Edinburgh pug *E. intricata* is reported to be numerous on the mountain juniper on Scalpay and South Rona but strangely the island in between, Raasay, apparently has none of the characteristic juniper moths. A few species of moths, mostly small in size, are found in conifer plantations. The larch pug *E. lariciata* is reported amongst larch on Canna and Rhum. Others in the region include the bordered white *Bupalus piniaria*, barred red *Ellopia fasciaria* and pine carpet *Thera firmata* which are probably more common than the records suggest. At least one moth of woodland habitat, the foxglove pug *Eupithecia pulchellata* has evolved into a separate island race var *hebudium* in which the generally reddish appearance is altered by the substitution of brown and white stripes.

Much less is known about other invertebrate life. In the social wasps the dark-coloured Norwegian wasp *Vespa norvegica* is more plentiful in the north of Britain and this together with the tree wasp *V. sylvestris* has been noted in Raasay woods, the former in some numbers; no doubt they are much more widespread. The greater horntail *Sirex gigas* with its accompanying parasitic Ichneumon *Rhyssa persuasoria* have been observed in abundance amongst pines on this island; these are insects which should increase with the continuing expansion of the Forestry Commission plantations. Two Orthopterons frequent the open woods; the common green grasshopper *Omocestus viridulus* is present on a number of the Inner Hebrides and on South Uist and the common ground-hopper *Tetrix undulata* occurs on Colonsay, Rhum and Barra. There are, inevitably, the common ground beetles of the woodland floor. Some years ago a surprising discovery was made near Tarbert on Harris of a tiny blue leaf beetle *Hermaeophaga mercurialis* which feeds on dog's mercury in woodland but until then was not known north of the Midlands. This is unlikely to have been either a deliberate introduction or one of a small resident colony overlooked before since the habitat is totally unsuitable. There remains the possibility that it was accidentally introduced with some plant material. A few observations of plant bugs have been made and these include shield, ground and capsid bugs. The rarest recorded bug in the Hebrides is a tiny flower bug *Anthocoris pilosus* which is a species of south-eastern Europe identified on Scalpay in the Inner Isles in 1936. One's first reaction is that this was an obviously accidental importation but there is some evidence that this species has been spreading north-westwards during this century.

BIRDS

The relatively small afforested area and the isolation of the islands means that one cannot take for granted the presence of all members of the typical woodland bird community. In addition there is some irregularity in breeding and birds may disappear from a particular island after nesting successfully for one or more years. If it were not for the woods at Stornoway the Outer Hebrides would be largely bereft of woodland species. These woods, after an initially slow colonisation, now have a rich resident avifauna. The Inner Hebrides being nearer the mainland and possessing more wooded areas can be expected to show a greater variety.

The creation of new plantations on moorland soon brings changes in the birdlife. For the first few years the small passerines of moorland are content to remain. Short-eared owls are partial to this habitat although they are rather scarce in the Hebrides; several pairs, however, were recorded in the woodland bird census on Rhum in 1974 and I have seen birds both in central Skye and on Mull. Another ground-nesting bird of young plantations and of the woodland edge is the black grouse which occurs on Islay and Mull. On the former island I have seen it on moorland where the only woods were stunted willow scrub. When the conifers have grown to the thicket stage lesser redpolls become typical birds and they nest on most of the larger Inner Isles; on Skye they are also present in the semi-natural hazel scrub. Another effect of coniferous afforestation has been to increase the numbers of such birds as song thrushes, robins and hedge sparrows. Goldcrests are characteristic birds of coniferous woods and are plentiful enough in this habitat; I have also observed them in willow scrub on Islay. In the tit family coal tits are more especially associated with plantations and are fairly common although they appear now to have disappeared from the Stornoway woods. Great, blue and long-tailed tits are well distributed in the mixed woods. The chaffinch, wren, blackbird and missel thrush are other common birds.

Of trunk-climbing birds there are tree-creepers and great spotted woodpeckers, the latter having begun to nest on a few of the Inner Hebrides. Ground-nesting birds include the pheasant which has been introduced to most of the Inner Isles. Another is that elusive bird the woodcock which, however, is not very plentiful and does not nest in the Outer Hebrides. On the Rhinns of Islay they nest in narrow belts of willow scrub and the local people believe that the birds which nest are not the same as those which winter there. The raucous cry of the jay is not heard nor is the harsh chatter of the magpie although the latter was once resident in the Inner Hebrides and a pair did nest on Skye in 1972. Hooded crows and jackdaws are not restricted to woodland but this is one of their habitats. There are a number of rookeries on some of the Inner Isles and a long-established one exists in the Stornoway woods with a population in 1973 of 195 pairs. It appears that in October 1893 an extraordinary mass migration of rooks took place across the Minch with hundreds dying on the western shores of Lewis. No less than 4,000 wintered in Stornoway that year; most of them departed in the following spring but about 200 remained to nest and a permanent population has resulted. Tawny owls are unexpectedly scarce and long-eared owls may perhaps equal them in numbers; the status of both species in the Outer Hebrides seems obscure but it appears that they nest at least occasionally at Stornoway. Kestrels and buzzards are fairly common in both island groups but are by no means confined to woodlands. Sparrowhawks are more restricted to this habitat; they breed on a number of the Inner but not the Outer Isles. Wood pigeons nest from Gigha to Stornoway although in the Outer Hebrides they are absent from North Uist southwards; in July 1972 one was even observed on the far outpost of North Rona.

A variety of migrants take up their summer quarters in the region although inevitably in smaller numbers than in southern Britain. The willow warbler is the commonest of the leaf warblers and is widespread in the Inner Isles. There used to be only sporadic and isolated occurrences of the chiff-chaff but in recent years they have spread northwards through a number of the Inner Hebrides. In June 1960 I heard one singing on Eigg but so far as I am aware there is no proof that they have as yet nested on the island; I have also heard them on Raasay where they have been known for a number of years and a wintering bird was discovered dead on Rhum in December 1972. The wood warbler is very scarce as there is little of its ideal habitat of tall deciduous trees available but it is occasional on one or two of the larger islands and has been seen in the Stornoway woods.

Common whitethroats used to be fairly numerous if somewhat local in the Hebrides but numbers have probably declined since the population crash of 1969 although in 1975 I saw birds in willow scrub on several of the Inner Hebrides. Blackcaps and garden warblers are in the main seen on passage. Other small migrants are spotted flycatchers, which reach part of the Outer Hebrides and are well distributed in the Inner; the tree pipit which summers only in the Inner Isles; and the redstart which is confined in general to Mull and Skye birch woods.

Winter visitors are few. There is an influx of woodcock in the autumn and very occasionally small numbers of brambling arrive in the deciduous woods. In irruption years crossbills spread westwards across Scotland and reach the Outer Hebrides; they have been seen on North Rona which has a good quota of vagrants. In the absence of conifers these birds are forced to feed on flower seeds.

MAMMALS

The effect of island fragmentation on small mammals is twofold. Firstly it means a scattered and irregular distribution of even common species and secondly it involves the development of sub-species. Two out of the four species of British shrews are present in some of the woodlands. The pygmy shrew can live in several habitats but one of the most favoured is the scrub growth which is so widespread. Perhaps partly as a consequence of this the mammal itself is well distributed on all the large islands. A surprising fact is that despite its early arrival in the Western Isles it has not only not evolved into a separate sub-species from the mainland shrew but has also not differentiated from the Continental animal. In contrast the common shrew has a tendency to separate into different races and as mentioned in Chapter One there is one such race on Islay although the other islands occupied by this mammal have the mainland stock. The common shrew is more typically a woodland animal and is not only present on Islay but also Gigha, Jura, Colonsay, Scarba, Mull, Ulva, Skye, Scalpay, Raasay and South Rona. Its absence from a number of other islands possessing the pygmy shrew indicates that it was a later arrival.

Of the voles the bank vole is essentially the woodland one but in the Hebrides it is known only from Mull and Raasay of which each has a distinctive race larger than the mainland form. It causes damage in plantations by barking young trees. The short-tailed vole is principally associated with cultivations but also occurs in small numbers in woodland and in the woods of Mull is reported to be most numerous in sections of spruce. The long-tailed field or wood mouse as its alternative names imply occurs in woods or fields with equal impartiality. The taxonomists have had a field day with this animal in the Western Isles and there are no less than nine varieties. The recent connection of Skye to the mainland is indicated by the presence of wood mice only of the mainland type. St Kilda has its own well defined sub-species while the remaining islands have the Hebbridean sub-species which has been further divided into a number of races. The islands possessing these are Gigha, Islay, Jura, Mull, Tiree, Rhum, Mingulay and Berneray.

The status of bats on the islands seems obscure and little information is available. It is probable that most of the larger wooded islands in the Inner Hebrides have one or two species such as pipistrelle, long-eared and possibly also Daubenton's but not in the numbers of southern Britain. Foxes are found only in Skye where they are reported to have increased considerably during World War II. In earlier centuries they were known on some other islands. There were also occupied badger setts on Skye but this mammal now appears to be extinct in the region. Fallow deer are very scarce occurring only in south-east Islay and Mull. They appear to have died out on Scarba some time after 1961. Roe are a little more widespread and have long been known in the wooded areas of north-east and south-east Islay and Seil; they have recently spread to the neighbouring island of Luing and to the Glen Brittle area of Skye.

CHAPTER SEVEN

Crofts and other agricultural land

Plants of field and machair—Invertebrates— Birds—Mammals

PLANTS OF FIELD AND MACHAIR

THE CROFTER HIMSELF AND the socio-economic aspects of crofting do not come within the scope of this book but the crofting system must interest any student of the local wildlife. Crofts have been defined as a type of 'specialised smallholding' and perhaps that is as good a definition as any. Their size varies from one acre to several hundreds although the latter is usually due to an amalgamation of several crofts. Three distinguishing features may be mentioned. The land is a kind of leasehold and the dwelling on it is not only provided by the tenant crofter but in many cases has been built by him or his forebears. The second factor is that the situation is governed by a succession of laws which date from 1886 and which give more legal rights to a croft than appertain to an ordinary smallholding. The third distinction lies in the communal nature of these land units which bears some resemblance to the manorial system in English agriculture under which each village had its common land. In the Hebrides today there are common grazings on the machair and the hilly ground outside the townships but the communal trait goes further than the mere sharing of common land for the crofters help each other in many co-operative tasks and have achieved a rare balance between a rugged individualism on the one hand and a true social concern on the other. Not all agricultural land is within the crofting system; some land consists of part arable, dairy and stock farms. Neither are all the agriculturalists Hebrideans for some are farmers from the Scottish Lowlands and others are Englishmen.

What of the crofter's attitude to wildlife? In the vast open spaces and in the absence of the sophistications of urban life the movement of birds and mammals around him naturally makes a greater impact than on the average town dweller. This does not necessarily mean that he is always knowledgeable about wildlife. Inevitably he views animals as they affect his crops and livestock rather than with a regard for their conservation. A situation has arisen in recent years, however, where nature conservation is of practical concern to the crofter. Few of them can make a full-time living from their crofts; some combine this with lobster-fishing, seaweed collection for the alginate industry, home crafts and other occupations. A not inconsiderable number are turning to tourism and since the type of holidaymaker who visits the Hebrides is often a country lover the preservation of the characteristic wildlife of the region is, or ought to be, of great interest to the crofter.

The crofting activities have their own effect on the flora. In some parts of the Outer Hebrides cultivation on the bare gneissose rock is not possible so lazybeds are constructed. These consist of layers of seaweed together with whatever scrapings of soil can be obtained which are piled on the rock; in some cases shallow soil is built up in strips by digging trenches between. The term 'lazybed' derives not from lazy but from ley, that is, untilled land. Yellow rattle *Rhinanthus minor* and marsh orchids *Dactylorchis* spp are typical plants of lazybeds. So much of the land surface is infertile moorland that the wind-blown calcareous shell-sand has come as a great boon and has made 'the desert blossom as the rose'. Efforts have been made in recent years to extend the area of fertile soil; in the 1960s 11,838 acres (4,794 hectares) were improved on Lewis by the application of eight tons (8·13 tonnes) of shell-sand per acre. A certain amount of arable cultivation is carried out on the machair with potatoes and oats. A relatively new industry is bulb growing on Mull, Tiree and North Uist.

The decline in population this century has meant that some land has ceased to be cultivated and the sites of these former cultivations are occupied by a miscellany of plants where invading moorland flowers have intermingled with arable weeds. The fields of Mingulay that once grew potatoes are now a carpet of silverweed *Potentilla anserina*, the deserted inbye land of South Rona has been encroached by moorland plants including rush *Juncus* spp, ling *Calluna vulgaris* and purple moor grass *Molinia caerulea*, old cultivations on Jura have been invaded by bracken *Pteridium aquilinum* whilst Dr Fraser Darling records that white clover *Trifolium repens* grows on former cultivated ground on North Rona.

Weeds of the arable fields are relatively few in species. Bristle or black oat *Avena strigosa* grows as a weed in the arable fields of Lewis. The most conspicuous wild flower which the casual observer cannot fail to notice is the corn marigold *Chrysanthemum segetum* which more than one botanist has described as colouring the fields on islands as far apart as Islay, Skye and Lewis. The common hemp-nettle *Galeopsis tetrahit* is of frequent occurrence and the yellow and violet blossoms of the large-flowered hemp-nettle *G. speciosa* are a typical sight on peaty, arable land. The common forget-me-not *Myosotis arvensis* has been noted as the most numerous weed in the barley fields of Barra but farther north on arable land at Uig in western Lewis it is less common and the dominant plant here is corn spurrey *Spergula arvensis*. That well known plant of cultivation, charlock *Sinapis arvensis* is abundant on Islay and Jura but less plentiful on Lewis. A northern species of dead nettle growing locally in the region is the intermediate dead nettle *Lamium molucellifolium*, a plant resembling henbit dead nettle but rather larger and with paler flowers. Other characteristic arable weeds which occur in varying quantities include wild radish *Raphanus raphanistrum*, corn sowthistle *Sonchus arvensis*, scentless mayweed

I

Tripleurospernum maritimum inodorum, redshank *Polygonum persi-caria*, fat hen *Chenopodium album* and several kinds of fumitory *Fumaria* spp.

Boggy pasture land supports a varied flora of moisture-loving plants such as flag iris *Iris pseudacorus*, cuckoo flower *Cardamine pratensis*, marsh marigold *Caltha palustris*, ragged robin *Lychnis flos-cuculi* and rushes *Juncus* spp. Yellow is the dominant colour of the flowers of Barra where I have seen a field of pink ragged robin rendered almost invisible by the even more numerous taller buttercups. The Hebridean orchid *Dactylorchis fuchsii hebridensis* is a sub-species of the common spotted orchid which is found only in the Hebrides. As the type species grows on limestone soils in southern England it is not surprising that the habitat of this flower is in the main restricted to the calcareous, often moist ground in the vicinity of the coastal dunes. It is shorter than the type and has distinctly deeper-coloured flowers. The early marsh orchid *D. incarnata* is another species with a preference for an alkaline habitat although it will tolerate mildly acid conditions; the flesh-coloured flowers of the commonest form are striking and make a refreshing change from the purple tones of so many other orchids. The northern fen orchid *D. purpurella* is essentially a northern species and in the Hebrides replaces the common marsh orchid *D. praetermissa* of southern Britain. This is a short-stemmed plant as one of its vernacular names implies and has brilliant red purple flowers. The Irish marsh orchid *D. majalis occidentalis* grows on Coll and Tiree and is the earliest flowering of all the marsh orchids. Another orchid from that country, the Irish lady's tresses *Spiranthes romanzoffiana* is found on Coll and Colonsay; it is abundant on some of the boggy pastures of the former island growing even in one locality along the roadside ditch. A fern typical of moist grassland in the region is the adder's tongue *Ophioglossum vulgatum* which although hard to find because of its small size and the fact that the parts above ground disappear by midsummer is present in most of the Outer Isles and on Islay, Colonsay, Tiree, Coll and Eigg.

The machair is a habitat to experience rather than to describe. Limestone grassland exists on Islay, Lismore and Skye but most of the calcareous grassland of the region consists of shell-sand machair which reach their greatest development on Tiree and the Outer Hebrides. It is a feature without parallel elsewhere in Britain. Although I have described the machair as grassland the general impression left upon the observer in July is of flowers other than grass. Grasses there certainly are with red fescue *Festuca rubra* sometimes the dominant species; others include meadow grass *Poa pratensis*, sweet vernal grass *Anthoxanthum odoratum*, cock's foot *Dactylis glomerata*, false oat *Arrhenatherum elatius* and Yorkshire fog *Holcus lanatus*. But it is the variegated carpet of blossom which catches the eye. There are the yellow of bird's foot trefoil *Lotus corniculatus*, kidney vetch *Anthyllis vulneraria*, silverweed *Potentilla anserina* and hawkbit *Leontodon autumnalis*; the blue of harebell *Campanula rotundifolia*, common milkwort *Polygala vulgaris* and germander speedwell *Veronica chamaedrys*; the purple of self-heal *Prunella vulgaris* and tufted vetch *Vicia cracca*; the white of common chickweed *Stellaria media*, purging flax *Linum catharticum*, daisy *Bellis perennis* and white clover *Trifolium repens*; the pink of red bartsia *Odontites verna* and stork's bill *Erodium cicutarium*; and the red of thyme *Thymus drucei* and red clover *Trifolium pratense*. Most of these plants are either naturally dwarf or wind-stunted. There are many more. Ragwort *Senecio jacobaea* is often abundant in other dry places as well as on the machair. In late July mushrooms are plentiful in some fields particularly on Mull, Muck and the Monachs. The little scarlet fungus *Hygrophorus coccineus* is fairly plentiful on the machair and other common fungi are the small species of *Coprinus* found on the dung of cattle. Most of the plants are admittedly run of the mill ones that can be seen all over Britain for the machair is not the place for the rarity hunter; it is the effect of common flowers en masse which is so spectacular. There is a small amount of arable cultivation but most of the machair is subject to grazing. Where this is excessive coarse plants such as stinging nettle *Urtica dioica* and thistles

Circium spp are likely to increase at the expense of other flowers more acceptable to domestic stock so that this practice is undesirable because it is self-defeating.

INVERTEBRATES

The extremely exposed conditions to which much of the Hebrides are subjected, especially the Outer Isles, results in an environment quite unsuitable for many invertebrates. The comparative paucity of the insect life is therefore to be expected and this scarcity is most pronounced in the Outer Hebrides. Not only are they more exposed but they were cut off from the mainland at an earlier date.

This is well illustrated by the Orthoptera. The separation into islands occurred before many of these insects could recolonise so that croft land in the Inner Hebrides has only three representatives and the Long Island only two; even these are of scattered distribution. The meadow grasshopper *Chorthippus parallelus* which is so common on the mainland is known only from some of the Inner Isles. The common green grasshopper *Omocestus viridulus* has a rather wider range occurring in a few places in the Outer Hebrides. The common ground-hopper *Tetrix undulata* is found on a few widely separated islands. The only earwig is the common species *Forficula auricularia* but this is exceedingly numerous on the machair and is present even on St Kilda.

The meadow brown *Maniola jurtina* is one of Britain's commonest butterflies with rough grassland as its haunt and during the summer it flies over croft land. It must be accounted a rather dull-looking insect but a brighter Hebridean variety occurs on a few islands as detailed in Chapter One. A much more local member of this family is the Scotch argus *Erebia aethiops* a northern butterfly of moist grassy areas which in the Hebrides frequents a restricted area centring on eastern Skye, Raasay, Scalpay and Mull. Another is the large heath *Coenonympha tullia* with a similar habitat preference to the preceding species but much more widespread being found also in the Outer Hebrides although not on every island. The green veined white *Pieris napi* has been mentioned in Chapter Five as a denizen of marshes but it can justifiably seek a place in this chapter being fairly common on the crofts on a number of islands. The small white *P. rapae* and the large white *P. brassicae* tend to fluctuate in numbers and have an erratic distribution due to their migratory habits. Of the Vanessids the peacock *Nymphalisio* used to be seen but I understand that it has virtually vanished from the region in recent years; the painted lady *Vanessa cardui* and red admiral *V. atalanta* are irregular migrants the visits of the former extending westwards to St Kilda; the small tortoise-shell *Aglais urticae* is a fairly widespread resident which has some colour variation in certain localities, for example, a rich-coloured form has been noted on Iona and Professor Heslop-Harrison in 1940 observed a large dark variety on Benbecula. The small copper *Lycaena phleas* has been recorded only from the Rhinns of Islay, Colonsay, southwest Mull and Ulva but it may yet appear on other islands for its range extends to north Scotland and there is plenty of its rough grassland habitat. The butterfly most evident on the machair is the common blue *Polyommatus icarus* and this widespread species can be seen in abundance on most of the islands.

A number of common moths frequent the machair, other grasslands and cultivated ground. The belted beauty *Nyssia zonaria*, the Hebridean speciality of dunes, is found on the machair and the caterpillars are sometimes present in great abundance. The grass rivulet *Perizoma albulata* is a common species on the Barra machair where the larvae feed on the seeds of yellow rattle. The dark arches *Apamea monoglypha* is well distributed and numerous on some islands; on Barra it has been reported as being probably the commonest moth on the island. Other common species of grassland include the common rustic *Mesapamea secalis* the larvae of which feed in grass stems and the antler moth *Cerapteryx graminis* whose larvae can denude considerable areas of grass. The silver Y *Autographa gamma* is an immigrant which sometimes swarms over various habitats and on Coll it has been seen visiting the flowers of Irish lady's tresses. The moths of cultivated ground include the magpie *Abraxis grossulariata*, garden tiger *Arctia caja*, garden carpet *Xanthorhoe fluctuata*, large yellow underwing *Noctua pronuba* and in neglected ground which is infested with nettles, the snout *Hypena probascidalis*.

Several kinds of bumble bees seek out the machair flowers although none is known on St Kilda. The visitor to the Hebrides will not escape the activities of the biting midges. Green- and blue-bottle flies may be noticed as they feed on carrion their brilliant metallic colouring glinting in the sunlight. Dung flies abound. Numbers of beetles with differing functions dovetail into the ecology of the crofts. Various species of ground beetles are plentiful and these are swift-running predators. A specialised predator of another family is *Phosphuga atrata* which feeds on the snails which are so abundant on the machair. Some beetles such as *Aphodius* spp live in and feed on the dung of cattle. Others are scavengers, notably the rove beetles of the large family of Staphylinidae. Conspicuous carrion feeders are the brightly-coloured burying beetles *Necrophorus* spp. Click beetles feed on plant roots whilst weevils consume the leaves. Another beetle which is a plant feeder is a chafer of sandy soils *Serica brunnea* which although a local species in Britain generally is reported as abundant on Barra machair and occurs also on Tiree and Rhum. This beetle was one which was noted by J. M. Boyd in an interesting study of the faunal differences between grazed and ungrazed land on Tiree as being favoured by the more temperate conditions of the ungrazed ground.

Apart from insects, other invertebrates include spiders, worms and molluscs. Harvestmen are often abundant on the machair and several kinds of wolf spider are present. A crab spider *Xysticus cristatus* is noted as plentiful on Barra and Tiree machair and is probably widespread in the Hebrides. The generally exposed situations are not very suitable for web-spinning spiders but where there is some shelter *Tetragnatha extensa* occurs and *Araneus diadematus* has been recorded commonly on Canna.

It is considered that worms must have been brought into the region in soil transported by man since it is unlikely that they could have survived the intense cold of the Pleistocene era. Earthworms require a deep rich moist soil so that it is a little surprising to find that several species are abundant on the machair but the moisture-laden winds are probably an important factor in providing sufficiently humid conditions; the numerous cow pats also provide moist conditions where worms congregate. The marsh worm *Lumbricus rubellus* is the dominant earthworm both on the machair and arable ground. It is not surprising that molluscs are present in quantity on the machair in view of their demand for calcium but the largest numbers are to be found where there is some protection from the winds. The common garden snail *Helix aspersa* is plentiful in grass and the turret-shaped *Cochlicella acuta* is widespread on the machair. There are many more and fifty-one species have been recorded from Barra.

BIRDS

The house sparrow, that common commensal of man and his habitations, is well distributed although one gets an impression that it is not as numerous as in many other parts of Britain; it has not always been resident in the Outer Hebrides and only began colonising Barra, for example, just before the beginning of the present century. It has now largely replaced the tree sparrow on Coll and Tiree. The status of the latter bird is obscure but it appears to be now extremely scarce. It is almost impossible to think of sparrows without also thinking of starlings for they are so often seen together both in rural and urban situations. This is a very common bird not only around the cottages and cultivations but also on the machair. The race inhabiting the Outer Isles is the Shetland starling but adults cannot be distinguished in the field from the type.

The corn bunting is a characteristic bird of cornfields in some parts of Britain. It has a patchy distribution in the Western Isles and is probably most common in the Outer Hebrides where it can be seen on the telephone wires singing its monotonous wheezy song. The greenfinch nests sparsely throughout both island groups but its numbers are considerably augmented in winter. The linnet and bullfinch nest sparingly in the southern part of the Inner Isles; I have seen a large flock of the former on Islay in late winter but it cannot really be accounted a Hebridean bird for its place is largely taken by its near relative the twite which is fairly common and widespread. The yellowhammer breeds locally but only in the Inner Hebrides. The machair in early summer is dotted with the nests of skylarks which with starlings and lapwings are the three common species there. These three alone are sufficient to make this western coastal strip vibrant with life as the starlings quarrel noisily on the ground, the lapwings tumble above them in exuberant abandon and higher still the lark serenely sings in an avian stratosphere.

The collared dove did not take long in arriving in the Hebrides but the colonisation was irregular and erratic. Birds were first seen in the Outer Isles in 1960 and were breeding at Stornoway by 1962. The first bird on Rhum was seen in May 1960, but not until four years later on Eigg. They arrived on Iona in 1963, bred on Islay in 1964 but did not reach Canna until 1970. Skye was colonised from 1964 onwards and the species is now widespread over the Western Isles. The barn owl probably nests fairly regularly on Islay and is occasionally seen elsewhere. Partridges have been introduced on various islands but in most cases have died out and Islay may be the only island still carrying a small stock. The breeding haunts of redshanks include wet meadows and this species is fairly well distributed in both island groups.

In addition to the starlings mentioned above there are three other species with Hebridean races which occupy croft land even if not always confined to this habitat. They are the song thrush, hedge sparrow and wren and brief details of these have already been given in Chapter One. A third sub-species of wren lives on St Kilda; it was described as a new species in 1884 but subsequently downgraded to sub-specific status. The St Kilda wren differs in several ways from the type; it is distinctly larger, has a paler breast, longer beak and a different song. It was inevitable that the announcement of a new species brought the unwelcome attention of egg collectors and one of the early Bird Protection Acts was enacted for the benefit of this bird in 1904. It has been estimated that there are about 230 pairs altogether on the islands of St Kilda.

The bird speciality of the crofts is without doubt the corncrake. This summer migrant has been the subject of a great decline on the mainland and the Hebrides are now its headquarters in Britain. Here it is still relatively common especially in the Outer Isles although it is not so plentiful as it formerly was and has now become very scarce on Mull. The harsh, rhythmic double call can be likened to the ringing of a telephone and when camping in the Outer Isles I have had half a dozen birds calling around the tent throughout the night, a memorable if sleep-disturbing experience. One might get the impression that the call is ventriloquial since the bird can seldom be located by going to the spot from where the sound is coming. The reason is not only that they turn their heads but also run at speed in a crouching posture through the long grass. When disturbed they prefer to disappear in this way rather than to fly; they fly on occasion and then the rich chestnut of their wings is revealed. Their eggs are often taken by rats. Other summer migrants are scarce. There are small numbers of swallows widely if somewhat irregularly distributed. House and sand martins are even scarcer and are virtually unknown in the Outer Hebrides. Sedge warblers are widespread in marshy ground; they are not always restricted to wet areas, however, and they have been seen inhabiting the barley fields of Gigha.

The advent of winter brings a change in the bird scene. Flocks of geese, barnacle, white-fronts, pink-footed and greylag descend from the skies to winter on the machair and the fields. These have already been referred to in more detail in Chapter Five. The crofters view their arrival with mixed feelings and their numbers on Islay are such that the agriculturalists are demanding a heavier culling of the barnacles. Flocks of golden plover join those of lapwing. Redwings and fieldfares are seen in large numbers on migration and some winter on the islands; the latter are widespread on both island groups but redwings occur mainly in the Inner Isles. Those that do visit the Outer Hebrides include some of the Icelandic race of redwings which are considered to be of a tamer disposition.

MAMMALS

House mice live out on the land during the summer and return to the dwellings and outbuildings in the winter; they have, for example, been seen on Colonsay half a mile from the nearest building. As mentioned in Chapter One St Kilda used to have a small and localised population of its own sub-species of house mouse centred around one or two of the dwellings. There was a slight difference of coloration and the animal had rather larger feet. As a commensal of man it was much affected by the evacuation of the island on 29 August 1930. It seems that as it was forced to forage farther afield it was unable to face competition from the larger, more aggressive field mouse and it soon became extinct. Reference to the status of the field mouse in the region has already been made in the previous chapter. Seton Gordon has recorded an old Lewisian belief that sand taken from Eilean Mealastadh off the west coast of Lewis and sprinkled on corn stacks would deter mice from eating the corn. It would be interesting to know the origin of such a strange belief.

The Hebridean short-tailed vole occurs on most of the islands although in the Outer Isles it is not found north of the Sound of Harris. The various island races of this mammal are listed in Chapter One. Brown rats abound on many islands but they are absent from some such as South Rona, Taransay, Pabbay in the Sound of Harris, North Rona and St Kilda. Moles are not indigenous and are only found on Skye and Mull. Hedgehogs are present on a number of islands including Coll, Mull, Canna and Skye but they are probably not native. Rabbits are plentiful on many islands especially on the machair; notable exceptions are Tiree, Muck and Rhum. Brown hares are exceptionally numerous in the grass fields of Islay and are present on some other islands. There are several mammalian predators on agricultural land. Feral polecat-ferrets have been seen on Mull in recent years; a number of the Inner Isles have stoats and weasels of which the former is the most widely distributed.

CHAPTER EIGHT

Hill and moorland

Moorland vegetation—Plants of wet moor and bog—
Mountain flora—Invertebrates—Birds—
Mammals and reptiles

MOORLAND VEGETATION

WHEN IN THE UISTS one moves eastwards from the machair to the moors there is a dramatic alteration in the surroundings. It is a change from shining clarity to sombre tones, from alkalinity to acidity, from a dry sandy soil to a wet peaty one. Only in early autumn does the vegetation lighten when the ling *Calluna vulgaris* comes into flower. If this environmental transformation is striking in the Uists it is even more so in Lewis where the backbone of the island is the gloomy Black Moor, a featureless waste of peat. There are many moors in the Inner Hebrides as well particularly on Jura, Mull, Coll, Rhum and Skye. The island with the lowest proportion of moorland is probably Tiree whose crofter inhabitants used to sail to Coll for their peat supplies as it was so scarce on their own island.

The overall impression of monotone is lessened when the plant community is examined more closely. The dominant shrub, of course, is ling which on some islands such as Eigg, grows to a great size. On dry areas, for instance, rocky outcrops, this is replaced by the earlier-flowering bell heather *Erica cinerea* but although relatively plentiful in many places it is always much less abundant than ling. It is, however, prevalent on Mull, and on Barra it has been observed to appear in areas where the ling has become old and coarse. The other ericaceous sub-shrubs of dry moor are generally scarce. Bilberry *Vaccinium myrtillus* is the commonest but it is not recorded from Tiree and is uncommon in the northern part of Lewis. Cowberry *V. vitis-idaea*, in Scotland often called cranberry, is rare; in the Outer Isles it is known only from the Harris hills and in the Inner it occurs only in a few widely scattered localities. The bearberry *Arctostaphylos uva-ursi* with its trailing stems and bright red berries is very localised but reported from most of the islands. Another creeping shrub whose linear leaves give it a superficial resemblance to the heathers is crowberry *Empetrum nigrum*; this is well distributed throughout the Western Isles but the other species *E. hermaphroditum* is quite rare. Gorse *Ulex europaeus* and broom *Sarothamnus scoparius* are probably not native in the Outer Isles and both shrubs are uncommon there; in the Inner Isles they are more common though never in abundance. On very exposed sites bracken is unable to tolerate the high winds but in certain localities it luxuriates to the detriment of agriculture.

There are certain flowering plants which are normally present on heather moors everywhere. They include the little heath milkwort *Polygala serpyllifolia*, a similar dwarf plant the heath lousewort *Pedicularis sylvatica* of rather damper spots, the tiny eyebright *Euphrasia officinalis*, devil's bit *Succisa pratensis*, heath bedstraw *Gallium saxatile* and tormentil *Potentilla erecta* which studs the moor with yellow dots throughout the summer. In the orchids the heath spotted *Dactylorchis maculata ericetorum* is often the only orchid found in this environment but it is abundant and widespread in both island groups. The brown-green flowers of lesser twayblade *Listera cordata* can be discovered under thick clumps of heather or bracken in some localities but it is scarce especially in the Inner Hebrides. Another orchid whose characteristic habitat is acid moorland is the lesser butterfly *Platanthera bifolia* with its strongly scented flowers which occurs sparingly in the Uists and on Harris; in the Inner Isles it is more widely distributed. The fragrant orchid *Gymnadenia conopsea* is another powerfully scented flower which grows on moors although it is quite catholic in its choice of situation; in the Inner Isles it is fairly widespread especially on Mull and Skye but in the Outer Isles it is known only from the small island of Fuday in the Sound of Barra.

Areas of dry grass moor are interspersed amongst the heather. The typical grass of the driest areas is the easily recognisable mat grass *Nardus stricta* with its flowers growing on one side of the stem. Other common sometimes abundant grasses include wavy hair grass *Deschampsia flexuosa*, common bent *Agrostis tenuis* and sheep's fescue *Festuca ovina*. A number of the flowering plants of heather moor are present here also but others are rather more typical of this habitat. They include fairy flax *Linum catharticum*, wild thyme *Thymus drucei*, slender St John's wort *Hypericum pulchrum*, autumnal hawkbit *Leontodon autumnalis* and cat's ear *Hypochoeris radicata*. The frog orchid *Coelgolossum viride* is locally plentiful but the small white orchid *Leucorchis albida* is known only from Mull, Coll, Rhum and Tiree.

PLANTS OF WET MOOR AND BOG

There is no arbitrary division of plants between dry and wet moor or between those of wet moor and bog because they often grade into one another and there is considerable overlap. Nevertheless, some distinction can be made. Purple moor grass *Molinia caerulea*, heath rush *Juncus squarrosus*, deer grass *Trichophorum cespitosum* and cross-leaved heath *Erica tetralix* are usually the basic constituents of wet moors in northern Britain and the last named has developed a variety of forms in southern Harris. Bog myrtle *Myrica gale* is a typical small shrub of wet moor in the Inner Hebrides but it is decidedly scarcer in the Long Island. A number of sedges are present and of these the star sedge *Carex echinata* and flea sedge *C. pulicaris* may be singled out as particularly numerous, the former being a sub-dominant of moor grass on Mingulay and Berneray.

In the boggier parts grow certain plants adapted to waterlogged conditions. The surface is carpeted with a floating mat of sphagnum from which arise white plumes of cotton grass of which two species are well distributed, the common *Eriophorum angustifolium* and the hare's tail *E. vaginatum*. Other members of the sedge family include the black bog rush *Schoenus nigricans*, white beak sedge *Rhyncospora alba* and numerous *Carex* spp. Two species of butterwort are present; the pale butterwort *Pinguicula lusitanica* is a plant of west and south-west distribution in the British Isles and it is well distributed in the Hebrides but it is scarcer than the earlier-flowering common butterwort. *P. vulgaris* which is the characteristic species of northern moors. The yellow spires of bog asphodel *Narthecium ossifragum* colour many a bog but the tiny bog pimpernel *Anagallis tenella* with its creeping stems can easily be overlooked; its neat little paired round leaves are almost as attractive in their way as the flowers. For sheer elegance the green-veined white flowers of grass-of-parnassus *Parnassia palustris* must surely hold pride of place in the bog flora; it is scattered throughout the Inner but does not exist in the Outer Hebrides. The bog orchid *Hammarbya paludosa* is a more inconspicuous flower and can be hard to find when buried under taller vegetation; it is very localised in the region but grows in various places in the Long Island and on Coll, Rhum and Skye. The round-leaved sundew *Drosera rotundifolia* is the commonest of this insectivorous genus but the other two species occur.

MOUNTAIN FLORA

Much of the Hebrides is hilly land above 500ft (152·4m) but few areas have land exceeding 2,000ft (609·6). The more mountainous localities are the Paps of Jura, Ben More on Mull, the mountains of Rhum, the Cuillins, the Storr and Quiraing on Skye, Ben More and Hecla on South Uist and the Harris hills. A great variety of plants grow in the rock crevices, ledges, gullies, screes and summit plateaux although by no means all of them are true mountain plants. On wet rock ledges, for example, may be seen many plants of meadow, moor and woodland.

Intermingling freely with these common plants are others which are more restricted to rocky terrain although in some instances a few of these alpines will grow at sea level. An interesting example of this is the moss campion *Silene acaulis* which is plentiful in certain places in western Lewis near the shore but is not found on the hills behind. In some other places such as the Storr and Quiraing on Skye and the mountains of Rhum and Mull it is typically a member of the high level plant community. This assemblage of alpines is notably rich bearing in mind that these are scattered islands isolated from the mainland flora. The explanation is that many of these arctic-alpines are relics of a pre-glacial period. Most of the islands excepting St Kilda were covered with glaciers and these mountain plants may not necessarily have survived in the localities where they now exist but may have migrated from land farther west which was not so affected by ice and which is now below sea level.

To gardeners the common rockery plants are saxifrages, stone-crops and rock-cress. Representatives of these three genera, some of them of great rarity, are to be found in the Western Isles. Three fairly common saxifrages of wet rocks are yellow mountain saxifrage *Saxifraga aizoides* found on moist rock ledges, starry saxifrage *S. stellaris* with a preference for the margins of running water at high altitude and rather more widespread than the former, and the purple saxifrage *S. oppositi-folia* with a similar distribution to the starry saxifrage but like the moss campion found also at very low levels. The mossy saxifrage *S. hypnoides*, too, appreciates a certain amount of moisture and grows in suitable habitat in the same hilly areas of the Inner Isles and also has been recorded from Coll; in the Outer Isles it appears to be known only from the eastern hills of South Uist. The gem of the genus is the alpine saxifrage *S. nivalis*, a rare plant growing in the islands only on the Storr and Quiraing on Skye and on Fionchra on Rhum. Stonecrops, though typical flowers of rock and stony ground are not really mountain plants but roseroot *Sedum rosea* with its fleshy glaucous leaves and large yellow flowers is a conspicuous member of the family in crevices in all the hilly areas. The only stations in Britain for the alpine rock-cress *Arabis alpina* are in the Cuillins where it is found very sparingly. This has white flowers with the

characteristic four petals of the family Cruciferae and is not a
very exciting plant. Here in the Cuillins a close relative the
northern rock-cress *Cardaminopsis petraea* grows in larger quantity; it is found elsewhere on Skye on the Storr, in the northern
part of Mull and on the Harris hills. Another member of this
family which in the Western Isles has only one known station,
on Fionchra, is alpine penny cress *Thlaspi alpestre*.

Alpine lady's mantle *Alchemilla alpina* is very localised in the
islands growing on some of the Inner Isles but on the Outer only
on the Clisham in Harris. It sometimes appears at low levels by
the side of burns where it has been washed down from higher
levels. The mountain avens *Dryas octopetala* is restricted to areas
of limestone and basic rocks; its foliage drapes over rocks on
several of the Inner Hebrides and on Skye it descends to a low
level. Other alpines of ledges and slopes include mountain everlasting *Antennaria dioica*, alpine saw-wort *Saussurea alpina*, alpine
meadow rue *Thalictrum alpinum*, mountain sorrel *Oxyrig digyna*,
alpine scurvy grass *Cochlearia alpina* and alpine willow herb
Epilobium anagallidifolium. The dwarf mountain form of the
common juniper *Juniperus communis nana* grows on many of the
islands but the type only in a few scattered places.

The plants of the fissures or grykes in the limestone pavements
of Skye cannot be designated mountain flora but nevertheless are
conveniently dealt with here. Perhaps the most interesting of
these is the dark red helleborine *Epipactis atrorubens* within the
region found only on Skye. Another orchid of this situation is
the common twayblade *Listera ovata*. The mountain avens is as
much at home here as it is at higher levels. Other flowering
plants include herb Robert *Geranium robertianum*, hairy rock-
cress *Arabis hirsuta*, common centaury *Centaurium erythraea* and
herb Paris *Paris quadrifolia* discovered in 1961 in Strath Suardal,
the only station in the region. Ferns revel in this habitat and here
will be found green spleenwort *Asplenium viride*, maidenhair
spleenwort *A. trichomanes*, hart's tongue *Phyllites scolopendrium*
and brittle bladder fern *Cystopteris fragilis*.

Ferns are also conspicuous components of stable screes. Com-
K

mon species like bracken *Pteridium aquilinium*, hard fern *Blechnum spicant*, lady fern *Athyrium filix-foemina*, male fern *Dryopteris filix-mas* and broad buckler fern *Dryopteris dilatata* are often abundant. The fern which is especially typical of screes, however, is parsley fern *Cryptogramma crispa*; this has a localised distribution in the Western Isles being known only from Mull, Rhum, South Uist and Harris. Where the rocks are acid in composition such as the quartzite screes of the Paps of Jura and the gneissose screes of the Uig district of western Lewis, ling is often dominant accompanied by various mosses. On talus in this latter area grows bearberry which has a preference for stony ground and amongst boulders here may be found bilberry, another member of the heather family. Both least cudweed *Gnaphalium supinum* and *Sibbaldia procumbens* are rare in the Hebrides but both occur on screes in northern Skye and possibly also in the Cuillins.

Whilst summit plateaux have a number of plants of other mountain habitats they have a specialised community of their own. Thrift *Armeria maritima* not only grows on coastal cliffs but also on inland summits. Moss campion, alpine saw-wort, mossy cyphel *Cherleria sedoides* and mountain azalea *Loiseleuria procumbens* are other members of this community though the last named is found within the region only on the Cuillin ridge. Stone bramble *Rubus saxatilis* is a characteristic plant of wet stony summits of limestone or basic rocks and it is well distributed over the ultra-basic mountains of southern Rhum. Mountain tops are the most exposed of all montane habitats and the Hebridean sites lack the prolonged snow cover of central Scotland. The stiff sedge *Carex bigelowii* and the three-flowered rush *Juncus triglumis* are fairly widespread on wet stony plateaux and on some islands are accompanied by the three-leaved rush *J. trifidus*, woolly fringe moss *Rhacomitrium lanuginosum* and the spiked woodrush *Luzula spicata*. The least willow *Salix herbacea* is the typical woody plant of the tops but more surprising is the record of two rowan seedlings found by Seton Gordon on the summit of Haskival, Rhum, 2,365ft (720·8m) above sea level.

The Hebridean summits have, in addition, two great rarities. The Iceland purslane *Koenigia islandica* is a tiny annual with no great claims to beauty but it is a glacial relict of relatively recent discovery; its only two stations in the British Isles are in the Hebrides on the Ardmeanach peninsula on Mull and on the Storr on Skye, in the latter locality it grows in some abundance. This plant was first found on the Storr in 1934 but was not identified until 1950. The Norwegian sandwort *Arenaria norvegica* is another inconspicuous rarity also discovered in the 1930s by a botanical team from Durham University on the summit of Ruinsival on Rhum; it is now known to occur on barren stony ground in a number of scattered localities from south-west Ireland to the Shetlands.

INVERTEBRATES

Only three members of the Orthoptera inhabit the Hebridean moors. The common ground-hopper *Tetrix undulata* and the mottled grasshopper *Myrmeleotettix maculatus* frequent dry heaths. The former is very localised; it is a dark-coloured insect, quite inconspicuous on the ground and may have a rather wider distribution than the records suggest. The mottled grasshopper is a little more widespread and its distinctive chirping can be heard on dry grass moors and on heather moors where the ling is short and interspersed with grass. It is found on Colonsay, Iona, Eigg, Rhum, Barra, where it is reported to be abundant, and South Uist. The wetter moors on some of the Inner Hebrides have the meadow grasshopper *Chorthippus parallelus*.

Summer sees a number of butterflies flying over the heather. That ubiquitous little insect the small heath *Coenonympha pamphilus* occurs all over the islands as does its bigger relative the large heath *C. tullia* in the sub-species *scotica*; Islay is the one island where in addition to *scotica* the type *tullia* has been noted. The one large fritillary of heath and moor is the dark green *Argynnis aglaia* which may be seen in July flying swiftly and powerfully over the heather on nearly all the islands. A large and dark sub-species called *scotica* is found in the Outer Isles and one or two Inner Isles and on the exposed island of Flodday near Barra Professor Heslop-Harrison discovered a small pale form of this butterfly which presumably had evolved into this small size in order to combat wind hazard. Two more July-flying butterflies are the common blue *Polyommatus icarus* which ranges from the coast to the hillsides and the grayling *Hipparchia semele* an insect of dry moor as well as of dunes.

Many kinds of moths frequent heather moors and even though there is rather less variety than on the mainland it is possible here to list only a few. Moors where sheep are not grazed or there is no heather burning have a richer insect fauna and P. Wormell, the Nature Conservancy Chief Warden on Rhum, has observed a considerable increase in the numbers of the drinker moth *Philudoria potatoria* when heather burning was stopped. An early flying moth of large and splendid appearance is the emperor *Saturnia pavonia* in which the sexes are well differentiated. The female is larger, differently coloured and flies at night in contrast to the day-flying habit of the male. A month or so later the northern oak eggar *Lasiocampa quercus callunae* and the fox moth *Macrothylacia rubi* emerge. Another day-flying but smaller moth with a more fluttering flight commonly seen in June is the common heath *Ematurga atomaria*. The magpie moth *Abraxas grossulariata* is plentiful on the moors where the caterpillars feed on ling in marked contrast to their partiality for gooseberry leaves in England.

Several species are particularly associated with bracken; the brown silver-line *Lithina chlorosata* has been noted on Canna together with the map-winged swift *Hepialus fusconebulosa* a moth of wider distribution the larvae of which feed on the roots of bracken. In dry areas on some islands where the wild thyme creeps over the rocks the caterpillars of the thyme pug *Eupithecia distinctaria* may be found in late summer and earlier; when one's foot treads upon the carpet of flowers, the moths themselves rise in the air together with the fragrance from the bruised foliage. In 1935 on a plant of thyme on Barra there was discovered a species of those primitive insects the springtails which was new to science.

Half of the British species of bumble bees occur in the Hebrides but the distribution of some species is sparse although it may be rather wider than the records suggest. The heath bumble bee *Bombus jonellus* which is typical though local in this habitat has been observed on Mull, Ulva, Skye, Raasay and North Uist; in the region it exists in the var *hebridensis*. Several of the carder bees occur and the distinctive member of this group in the Hebrides is Smith's carder bee *B. smithianus* which in Britain is known only on islands; in the Western Isles it is especially common in the Long Island and is also present on Coll, Tiree and Rhum.

Beetles of moorland can be divided into the plant-eaters, dung and carrion feeders and carnivores. Two characteristic species which feed on ling are the heather weevil *Micrelus ericae* and the heather beetle *Lochmaea suturalis* which has been recorded up to the 2,000ft (609·6m) level on Rhum. Winter losses of sheep provide carrion feeders with rich pickings and prominent amongst them are the ground beetles. Although large beetles of the genus Carabus are not very plentiful on some islands there are others of this family such as *Pterostichus* spp, *Notiophilus* spp and the small copper-coloured *Elaphrus cupreus*. Another is *Cychrus caraboides* a large black beetle of elegant appearance reported from the summit of Heaval on Barra and on the slopes of Hallival on Rhum. Two rare Carabids have been reported from mountainous ground on Rhum; the rarest is *Amara quenseli* known elsewhere in Britain only from a few mountains on the Scottish mainland; the other is *Leistus montanus* a beetle which is more widespread, though it is scarce in hilly regions, of Britain from North Wales northwards.

Since exposure is such an important factor in the Hebrides, many of the spiders are those which have adapted themselves to the environment either by living in rock crevices, under stones or in other sheltered conditions. *Segestria senoculata* is the only common member of its genus and is fairly widespread on the islands living in crevices. Equally common in this situation is *Meta merianae* which elsewhere in Britain can be found also on vegetation. The wolf spiders *Lycosa* spp are typical of those which live under stones and the very local northern species *L. traillii* has been noted from the Red Hills of Skye. The pirate spider *Pirata piraticus* is fairly common on boggy moors being recorded from Colonsay, Eigg, Canna, Barra and St Kilda and it may well be more widely distributed. Nearly all the Hebridean spiders are common kinds but a rare species of grass and moss, *Meioneta beata*, was first discovered in Scotland on the Garvellachs by Dr Bristowe.

A specialised invertebrate fauna frequents the mountain summits. Mention has already been made of several ground beetles in this habitat. The weak-flying stoneflies often live under stones usually within a short distance of the burn where they existed in their larval state and several of the stonefly *Protonemura meyeri* have been recorded amongst boulders near the summit of Hallival on Rhum. The summit of Ben-na-Caillich on Skye has an arctic spider *Leptyphantes whymperi* together with another in the genus *L. zimmermanni* which although often found on low ground is also frequent on mountains. The Cuillins of Skye provide a particularly harsh environment and on the summit of Sgurr Dubh-Nada-dheinn Dr Bristowe located but three species of spider, all three montane in character, *Hilaira frigida* and *Collinsia holmgreni* which are arctic in origin and *Wideria capito* a species of the Welsh mountains and of the Lake District.

BIRDS

Moorland seldom teems with birdlife and many localities appear almost bereft of birds. Nevertheless, over thirty species are regular moorland breeders in the Hebrides. Familiar sounds in summer are the song of the soaring skylark and that which passes for song from the more prosaic meadow pipit. These birds, resident over much of Britain, are only summer visitors to the Western Isles. The linnet always seems associated with gorse and the markedly local status of linnets in the Inner Isles and their extreme scarcity in the Outer Isles is perhaps partly related to the paucity of gorse. Its close relative the twite is much more common and is most numerous in the Outer Hebrides. A very pleasant birding memory is of sitting in a hide on the Long Island with a twite pouring out his song whilst perched on the roof only a few inches above my head. Wheatears are very plentiful but prefer the rocky areas and those honeycombed with rabbit burrows rather than dense moorland vegetation. Stonechats and whinchats, too, are common; of the two, the latter is less widespread frequenting grass, bracken and gorse localities especially on some of the Inner Hebrides. Ring ouzels are birds of rocky moorland; they are very uncommon in the islands but a few pairs nest on Mull, in the corries of Rhum, on the peninsula of Trotternish in northern Skye and possibly also on Raasay. Both blackbird and song thrush frequent the moors, perhaps more so in the Hebrides than on the mainland; in a North Harris valley I have heard rival song thrushes singing on cliffs half a mile apart. The Hebridean wren is typically found in heathery, rocky situations. In winter the little snow buntings haunt some of the hills but are more widespread during migration. Baxter and Rintoul state that the only known record of breeding in the Outer Hebrides was a nest on St Kilda in 1913 although summering birds have occasionally been seen in the Long Island. Cuckoos are well distributed in summer.

Of the game birds red grouse are reasonably common but black grouse, as mentioned in Chapter Six, are much less so. The red grouse inhabiting the Outer Isles belongs to the Irish race although there have been introductions of British red grouse. In the last century ptarmigan bred on some of the hills from Islay to Lewis. The hills in south-east Islay are well below the level at which these birds are usually found but a brood was reared there as late as 1936 and on the Paps of Jura in 1939. Ben More on Mull has been a last stronghold although there are reports of birds being seen occasionally in some of their old Hebridean haunts in recent years and they may yet breed again.

A number of wading birds arrive on the moors in spring to
breed. The curlew is such a characteristic bird of moors on the
mainland that it comes as a surprise to find that there are some
islands where it does not nest such as the Small Isles and most of
the Long Island. Its close relative the whimbrel is a rare bird
whose main breeding haunts in Britain are in the Shetlands but
the odd bird is occasionally seen on Lewis and a nest was recorded on St Kilda in 1964. The plaintive call of the golden
plover can be heard on most of the moors where nesting territories are often at quite low levels; it is however a very scarce
nester in the Small Isles and is not known to nest on Tiree, Coll
or Barra. Outside the nesting season flocks arrive to spend the
winter in the region. The greenshank is generally a scarce nester
on a few islands in both groups although it seems fairly common
on Harris. The dunlin not only nests on the machair but on the
moors as well; it is much more abundant in the Outer Isles and
is absent as breeder from most of the Inner Isles. The common
snipe is very plentiful on boggy moorland throughout the
islands; the snipe occurring on St Kilda is the sub-species of the
Faeroe Islands and is reported to prefer drier habitats than the
common snipe. The jack snipe is a winter visitor in fluctuating
numbers.

Three species of seabirds, apart from gulls, nest inland, two of
them on moorland and one on mountain summits. Enormous
colonies of Manx shearwaters nest on the mountains of Rhum
breeding up to 2,365ft (720·8m) on Hallival and up to two miles
inland. In 1974 some 30,000 pairs were recorded. The Nature
Conservancy are at present engaged in a study of the populations
and ecology of these colonies. Arctic skuas occur in small colonies
on Jura and Coll in the Inner Hebrides and in the northern half of
the Long Island. They haunt the Harp Rock of Lunga in the
Treshnish Isles and prey on the seabirds there. Great skuas have
a more restricted distribution in the region nesting in Lewis and
St Kilda but there are indications that it is extending its range.

There is a variety of predators although most are not numerous. The hooded crow is plentiful enough and the raven is not

scarce. The kestrel and merlin have a contrasting distribution pattern. The former is more common in the Inner Isles while the latter is more plentiful in the Outer group. Buzzards are widespread although on one or two islands they nest only occasionally. Golden eagles are found on nearly all the islands which have high hills but this does not mean that they only nest at high altitude for they sometimes nest on quite low hills and coastal cliffs. They are looked upon with great suspicion by many of the crofters. One retired North Uist keeper told me in 1967 that in the spring of that year he had seen an eagle swoop down and snatch a lamb from the ewe's side. Such instances, however, are rare. In the spring of 1954 complaints were made that many lambs were being taken by eagles in the Uig district of Lewis. An investigation was made by J. D. Lockie and D. Stephen who considered that most lambs taken were probably carrion; they in fact saw in an eyrie only one lamb which had been killed by an eagle. They found that the usual prey, rabbits, mountain hare and red grouse were sparse and that conversely there was a high density of sheep. Their conclusion was that a change in land management should be implemented by reducing the stock of sheep rather than shooting eagles which would merely leave territories vacant for other pairs to move in and take over. Hen harriers are very scarce but are found in the Outer Hebrides especially on South Uist; they are beginning to appear on one or two of the Inner Hebrides in recent years. That speciality of the Shetlands, the snowy owl, does not yet nest in the region but several were observed in the Outer Isles in 1972 and '73.

REPTILES AND MAMMALS

The Outer Hebrides not only lack amphibians but have only one reptile, the slow-worm, which is found there in scattered colonies; it is rather more widespread in the Inner Hebrides. Most of the larger islands of this group have the common lizard as well although it does not appear to be very common. The only snake represented is the viper which is fairly common on the larger Inner Isles and occurs on the small island of Scarba as well.

Some small mammals such as voles, shrews and mice are found on moorland and details of their distribution have been given in earlier chapters. The mainland form of the field mouse which occurs on Skye has been noted even on the Cuillins. An unexpected event in 1971 was the definite sighting of a pine marten on Raasay. They were formerly present in both island groups and there is a macabre account from Harris of a marten and sheep being found dead, the former's teeth sunk deep into the sheep's throat; the panic-stricken sheep must have rushed into a rock killing itself and the marten. Wild cats do not now occur although they are reported to have existed on Skye up to the last century and in 1960 a wild cat kitten was caught swimming in the Sound of Sleat.

Brown hares frequent moors as well as pasture land and I have seen them commonly amongst heather on Islay. All the present stock of mountain hare is probably derived from introduced animals but they may well have been indigenous in the past. In the case of some islands the introduction dates are known; the Scottish race was introduced to Harris in 1859, to Mull in 1864, to North Uist about 1890, to Eigg between 1890 and 1900 and to Jura about 1908. R. Hewson in 1955 made a survey of the distribution of the mountain hare in the region. Three islands where the Scottish mountain hare is still fairly common are Mull, Raasay and the northern part of Jura. They were present on the Cuillins in the last century but they are now reported as very scarce on Skye. They are very uncommon or rare on Scalpay (Skye), North Uist, Harris and Lewis and extinct on Islay and Eigg. The Irish race was introduced to Islay and Mull; they have long been extinct on the former island but it is believed that small numbers may still be present in the northern part of Mull.

Red deer live on a number of islands. In the Inner Hebrides they are found on the moorlands of eastern Islay, on Jura, Scarba, Mull, Rhum, Skye, Scalpay and Raasay. In the Outer Isles they are present on North Uist, Pabbay, Harris and Lewis.

The largest populations are on Jura and Rhum; a census on the former island in 1969 produced a total of 5,435. It was not for nothing that the roving Norsemen gave the island the name Dyrey meaning deer island. For some reason the Jura stags have a relatively high proportion of animals with malformed antlers known as 'cromies'. The sea barrier does not entirely confine red deer and there is a certain amount of movement between Jura and Islay and between Pabbay and North Uist. In recent years additions have been made to the stock on a few islands.

The problems of island living, especially in the Hebrides, are many but it is probably true to say that at the present time both the islanders and Government bodies are more alert to the dangers and more conscious of the possibilities, than at any time in the past. A start has been made in the development of much-needed local industries appropriate to the region. The islander, however, is not likely to accept anything which seriously conflicts with the traditional way of life or mars the beauty of the landscape. The naturalist and the lover of wild and lonely places can generally be assured of a hospitable welcome from the Hebridean crofter who is rightly proud of his heritage.

Appendix

Access

This is straightforward in the case of the larger islands but where the smaller, more remote islands are concerned, access is not always easy. Some islands are much more accessible than others but services naturally operate subject to weather conditions. Since timetables are liable to alteration these details are left for the individual enquirer to obtain for himself from the addresses listed below.

British Airways (Scottish Airways), 122 St Vincent Street, Glasgow C2
Caledonian MacBrayne Ltd, The Pier, Gourock PA19 1QP
Loganair Ltd, Glasgow Airport, Abbotsinch, Glasgow
Western Ferries Ltd, Kennacraig, Tarbert, Argyllshire, Strathclyde

Routes

It will be appreciated that these, too, may be subject to change.
Inner Hebrides
Gigha   passenger ferry from Tayinloan on the Kintyre peninsula
   MacBrayne's car ferry from West Loch Tarbert (summer)
Islay   MacBrayne's car ferry from West Loch Tarbert to Port Ellen
   Western Ferries car ferry from Kennacraig, Tarbert to Port Askaig
   BEA from Glasgow
Jura No direct access from the mainland; entry from Islay via Western
   Ferries car ferry from Port Askaig to Feolin
Colonsay MacBrayne's steamer from Oban
Scarba Boat hire from Black Mill Bay on Luing
Luing   Car ferry from Seil
Seil Road bridge from mainland
Easdale Passenger ferry from Seil
Garvellachs Boat hire from Cullipool on Luing (permission for landing
   required)
Kerrera Passenger ferry from Lorn, near Oban

Lismore MacBrayne's passenger ferry (cars by arrangement) from Oban
    Passenger ferry from Port Appin
Mull MacBrayne's car ferry from Oban to Craignure
    MacBrayne's car ferry from Oban to Tobermory
    MacBrayne's car ferry from Lochaline to Fishnish
    MacBrayne's passenger ferry from Lochaline to Craignure
    MacBrayne's passenger ferry from Mingary to Tobermory
    Loganair from Glasgow and Connel to Glen Forsa, near Salen
Iona MacBrayne's passenger ferry from Fionnphort, Mull
    MacBrayne's excursions from Oban
Staffa MacBrayne's excursions from Oban (no landing)
    Boats from Kellan Mill (Mull), Penmore, Croig (Mull) and Ulva Ferry
    (Mull)
Ulva Boat from Ulva Ferry (permission must be obtained beforehand from
    the Manager Mr Hugh McPhail)
Gometra By bridge from Ulva
Treshnish Isles Boats from Penmore, Croig (Mull) and Ulva Ferry (Mull)
Tiree MacBrayne's steamer from Oban, Lochaline, Tobermory and Coll
    BEA from Glasgow
Coll MacBrayne's steamer from Oban, Lochaline, Tobermory and Tiree
    Loganair from Glasgow (summer)
Muck MacBrayne's steamer from Mallaig
    Motor boat from Galmisdale, Eigg
    Excursions by *Royal Scot* from Arisaig
Eigg MacBrayne's steamer from Mallaig
    Excursions by Bruce Watts' motor vessels from Mallaig
    Excursions by *Royal Scot* from Arisaig
Rhum MacBrayne's steamer from Mallaig
    Excursions by Bruce Watts' motor vessels from Mallaig
    Excursions by *Royal Scot* from Arisaig
    (Note that access on Rhum is restricted to area around Loch Scresort)
Canna MacBrayne's steamer from Mallaig
    Excursions by Bruce Watts' motor vessels from Mallaig
Skye Car ferry from Glenelg to Kylerhea
    MacBrayne's car ferry from Kyle of Lochalsh to Kyleakin
    MacBrayne's car ferry from Lochmaddy, North Uist and Tarbert, Harris
    to Uig
    MacBrayne's car ferry from Mallaig to Armadale
    Loganair from Glasgow
Raasay MacBrayne's steamer from Portree, Skye
    Passenger ferry from Sconser, Skye
South Rona Excursions from Portree (no landing)

Soay   Boat by arrangement from Loch Brittle, Skye

Outer Hebrides

Mingulay   Excursions from Castle Bay, Barra

Vatersay   Passenger ferry from Castle Bay, Barra

Barra   MacBrayne's car ferry from Oban
     MacBrayne's car ferry from Lochboisdale, South Uist
     BEA from Glasgow to Northbay
     Loganair from Glasgow to Northbay

Eriskay   Excursions from Castle Bay, Barra
     Passenger ferry from Ludag, South Uist and by arrangement from Eoligarry, Barra

South Uist   MacBrayne's car ferry from Oban and Castle Bay, Barra to Lochboisdale
     Bridge from Benbecula

Benbecula   No direct access by sea from the mainland
     MacBrayne's car ferries either from Oban to Lochboisdale, South Uist or from Uig, Skye to Lochmaddy, North Uist
     BEA from Glasgow and Stornoway, Lewis
     Loganair from Glasgow and Stornoway, Lewis

North Uist   MacBrayne's car ferry from Uig, Skye and Tarbert, Harris
     Bridge from Benbecula
     Passenger ferry from Leverburgh, Harris to Newton

Berneray   Passenger ferry from Newton, North Uist and Leverburgh, Harris

Harris   MacBrayne's car ferry from Uig, Skye and Lochmaddy, North Uist

Taransay   Boat from Horgabost, Harris by arrangement with the boat owner on Taransay

Scalpay   MacBrayne's car ferry from Kyles Scalpay, Harris

Scarp   Boat from Husinish, Harris by arrangement with Mr McLennan of Scarp

Shiant Isles   Boat charter from Mr McLeod of Scalpay

Lewis   MacBrayne's car ferry from Ullapool to Stornoway
     Bus from Tarbert, Harris
     BEA from Benbecula, Glasgow, Inverness to Stornoway
     Loganair from Benbecula and Glasgow to Stornoway

Great Bernera   Bridge from Crulivig, west Lewis

NATURE RESERVES

Since the whole region is of natural history interest it is hardly feasible to follow the pattern of previous books in this series and list specific areas. There are, however, several nature reserves and these are set out below.

Inner Hebrides

Rhum The whole island has been a National Nature Reserve since 1957 and comprises 26,400 acres (10,692 hectares). There is a rich and varied plant and animal life with alpines, rare moths, large shearwater colonies, auks, golden eagles, red deer and wild goats. There are two nature trails, the South Side and Kinloch Glen. Access for the general public is restricted to day visits to the eastern area around Loch Scresort and only scientists, naturalists and mountaineers are allowed to stay longer on the island after obtaining permission from the Nature Conservancy.

Outer Hebrides

Loch Druidibeg, South Uist This is a National Nature Reserve and Wildfowl Refuge comprising an area of machair as well as the loch with its many islands. The area totals 4,148 acres (1,680 hectares). The reserve was primarily established to protect the largest breeding area in Britain of the greylag goose. There is much else of interest including relict scrub vegetation. Access restricted during the breeding season.

Monach Isles These comprise five sandy islands and were established as a National Nature Reserve in 1966. Many plants of machair and colonies of seabirds including terns.

Balranald, North Uist A bird reserve of the Royal Society for the Protection of Birds. Birds of many species abound. The three lochs carry a number of nesting waterfowl. Corncrakes are plentiful but the principal interest of the reserve was the red-necked phalarope. This has, however, become extremely scarce and failed to breed in 1973. The offshore islet of Causamul with its nesting seabirds and breeding Atlantic grey seals is also a part of the reserve. The warden should be contacted before entering the reserve.

St Kilda A National Nature Reserve of 2,107 acres (853 hectares) leased from the National Trust for Scotland. A group of islands with great natural treasures including the largest gannetry in the world, enormous numbers of other seabirds, some endemic animals and, considering its oceanic situation, a rich vegetation.

North Rona and Sula Sgeir These two remote islands form one National Nature Reserve totalling 320 acres (129·6 hectares). North Rona was established because of its importance as an Atlantic grey seal breeding station and for its nesting population of Leach's fork-tailed petrel. Sula Sgeir has a large gannet colony.

Bibliography

Anderson, A., Bagenal, T. B., Baird, D. E., Eggeling, W. J.
'A Description of the Flannan Isles and their Birds', *Bird
Study*, 8 (1961), 71–88

Andrew, Dougal G. and Sandeman, Gerard L. 'Notes on the
Birds of the Flannan Isles', *Scot Nat*, 65 (1953), 157–66

Asprey, G. F. 'The Vegetation of the Islands of Canna and
Sanday, Inverness-shire', *Jnl Ecol*, 34 (1947), 182–93

Atkinson, R. 'Notes on the Botany of North Rona and Sula
Sgeir', *Trans Soc Bot Edin*, 30 (1940), 52–60

——. *Island Going* (1949), Collins

Atkinson, R. and Roberts, B. 'Notes on the islet of Gasker',
Scot Nat, 64 (1952), 129–37

Bagenal, T. B. and Baird, D. E. 'The Birds of North Rona in
1958 with notes on Sula Sgeir', *Bird Study*, 6 (1959), 153–74

Balfour-Browne, F. 'Contribution towards a list of the Insect
Fauna of the South Ebudes I Aquatic Coleoptera', *Scot Nat*
(1923), 53–60

——. 'The Aquatic Coleoptera of the Outer Hebrides', *Scot Nat*
(1938), 33–46

Barkley, S. Y. 'The Vegetation of the Island of Soay, Inner
Hebrides', *Trans Bot Soc Edin*, 36 (1953), 119–31

Baxter, E. V. and Rintoul, L. J. *The Birds of Scotland* (Edinburgh,
1953), Oliver & Boyd

Bertram, D. S. (Ed) 'The Natural History of Canna and Sanday,
1936 and 7', *Proc Royal Physical Soc Edin*, 23 (1939), 1–71

Blackburn, K. B. and Lobley, E. M. 'Some Bryophytes of the
Small Isles Parish of Inverness-shire and of the Island of
Soay', *Durham Phil Soc*, 10 (1939), 130–40

Bourne, W. R. P. 'Birds of the Island of Rhum', *Scot Nat*, 69 (1957), 21–31

Boyd, J. M. 'Lumbricidae in the Hebrides II Geographical Distribution', *Scot Nat*, 68 (1956), 165–72

——. 'Ecological Distribution of the Lumbricidae in the Hebrides', *Proc Roy Soc Edin*, B 66 (1957), 311–38

——. 'The Birds of Tiree and Coll', *Brit Birds*, 51 (1958), 41–56, 103–18

——. 'Studies of the differences between the fauna of grazed and ungrazed grassland in Tiree', *Proc Zool Soc Lond*, 135 (1960), 33–54

——. 'Grey Seal in the Outer Hebrides in October, 1961', op cit, 141 (1964), 635–61

Bristowe, W. S. 'The spider fauna of the Western Islands of Scotland', *Scot Nat* (1927), 88–94, 117–22

Brooke, M. de L. 'The Puffin Population of the Shiant Islands', *Bird Study*, 19 (1972), 1–6

——. 'Birds of the Shiant Islands', op cit, 20 (1973), 221–5

Campbell, J. L. 'Macrolepidoptera of the parish of Barra', *Scot Nat* (1938), 153–63

——. 'Macrolepidoptera of the Isle of Canna', op cit, 66 (1954), 101–21

——. 'The Butterflies and Moths of Canna', *Ent Record* 82 (1970), 211–14, 235–42, 292–9: 83 (1971), 6–12

——. '*Mythimna unipuncta* and other Lepidoptera on the Isle of Canna', op cit, 85 (1973), 298

Campbell, M. S. (Ed) *The Flora of Uig (Lewis)* (Arbroath, 1945), Buncle

Carrick, R. and Waterson, G. 'Birds of Canna', *Scot Nat* (1939), 5–22

Clark, W. A. 'The Flora of the Islands of Mingulay and Berneray', *Proc Durham Phil Soc* 10 (1938), 56–70

——. 'Noteworthy Plants from North Uist, Baleshire, Monach Islands, Harris, Taransay, Mingulay and Berneray', op cit, 10 (1939), 124–9

L

——. 'Plant Distribution in the Western Isles', *Proc Linn Soc*, 167 Pt 7 (1954), 96–103

Clark, W. A. and Harrison, J. H. 'Noteworthy Plants from Great and Little Bernera (Lewis), Pabbay and Berneray (Harris) and the Uig district of Lewis', op cit, 10 (1940), 214–21

Cuthbert, J. H. 'The Origin and Distribution of Feral Mink in Scotland', *Mammal Review*, 3 No 3 (1973), 97–103

Darling, F. F. *A Naturalist on Rona* (Oxford, 1939), Clarendon Press

Darling, F. F. and Boyd, J. M. *The Highlands and Islands* (Collins, 1964)

Dawson, R. 'Island of Geese', *Birds* 5 (1975), 22–3

Delaney, M. J. 'Ecological Distribution of Small Mammals in North-west Scotland', *Proc Zool Soc Lond*, 137 (1961), 107–26

Delaney, M. J. and Copland, W. O. 'Effects of depopulation on the island of South Rona', *Glasgow Naturalist*, 18 (1964), 351–62

Dennis, Rev Norman. 'Records of Non-vascular Cryptograms on Skye', *Trans Bot Soc Edin*, 40 (1966), 204–31

Dennis, R. W. G. 'Contribution towards a Fungus Flora of the Small Isles of Inverness', *Trans Bot Soc Edin*, 36 (1952), 58–70

Diamond, A. W., Douthwaite, R. J., Indge, W. J. E. 'Notes on the birds of Berneray, Mingulay and Pabbay', *Scottish Birds*, 3 (1965), 397–404

Eggeling, W. I. 'Check List of the Plants of Rhum', *Trans Bot Soc Edin*, 40 (1965), 20–99

Evans, P. R. and Flower, W. U. 'The birds of the Small Isles', *Scottish Birds*, 4 (1967), 404–45

Elton, Charles. 'Notes on the Ecological and Natural History of Pabbay and other Islands in the Sound of Harris', *J Ecol*, 26 (1938) 275–297

Fisher, J. (Ed), *New Naturalist Journal* (1948), Collins

Fisher, J. *The Fulmar* (1952), Collins.
   Rockall (1956), Bles
Flegg, J. J. M. 'The Puffins of St Kilda', *Bird Study*, 19 (1972), 7–17
Forrest, J. E., Waterston, A. R., and Watson, E. V. 'The Natural History of Barra', *Proc Roy Phy Soc Edin*, 22 (1936), 241–96
Gillham, M. E. 'Coastal Vegetation of Mull and Iona in relation to salinity and soil reaction', *J Ecol*, 45 (3) (1957), 757–78
Gimingham, C. H., Miller, G. R., Grieg-Smith, P. 'Vegetation of sand-dune systems in the Outer Hebrides', *Trans Bot Soc Edin*, 35 (1948), 82–96
Gordon, Seton. *Highland Summer* (Cassell, 1971)
Grimshaw, P. H. 'Notes on the Insect Fauna of South Uist', *Scot Nat* (1920), 85
Hall, Rev J. H. Vine. 'Some notes on Lepidoptera from the Hebrides', *Ent Gaz*, 20 (1969), 53–58
Harrison, J. H. 'Recent Researches on Flora and Fauna of the Western Isles of Scotland and their Biogeographical Significance', *Proc Belfast Nat Hist and Phil Soc*, Series 2, Vol 3, Pt 2 (1947), 87–96
Harrison, J. W. H. 'Natural History of Raasay and of the adjoining islands', *Durham Phil Soc*, 9, Pt 5 (1937), 246–351
——. 'The Fauna and Flora of the Inner and Outer Hebrides', *Nature*, 143 (1939), 1004–6
——. 'A Preliminary Flora of the Outer Hebrides', *Proc Durham Phil Soc*, 10 (1940), 228–308
——. 'More Hebridean Days II: The Isle of Benbecula', *Ent*, 74 (1941), 1–5
——. 'The Fauna and Flora of the Inner and Outer Hebrides', *Nature*, 147 (1941), 134–6
——. 'Potamogetons in the Scottish Western Isles', *Trans Bot Soc Edin*, 35 (1948), 1–25
——. 'Contribution to our knowledge of the Flora of the Isles of Lewis, Harris, Killegray and Ensay', *Trans Bot Soc Edin*, 35, Pt 2 (1949), 132–56

——. 'Occurrence of the American pondwood *Potamogeton epihydrus* in the Hebrides', *Nature*, 169 (1952), 548–9

Harrison, J. W. H. and Blackburn, K. B. 'Occurrence of a nut of *Trapa natans* in the Outer Hebrides with some account of peat bogs adjoining loch', *New Phytologist*, 45 (1946) 124–31

Hewer, H. R. *Grey Seals* (1962), *Sunday Times*

Hewson, R. 'The Mountain Hare in the Scottish Islands', *Scot Nat*, 67 (1955), 52–60

Hunter, W. R. 'Notes on the Mollusca of the Garvelloch Islands', *J Conchology*, 23 (1953), 379–86

——. 'New and newly confirmed distribution records of non-marine molluscs in the West of Scotland', *Glasgow Nat*, 17 (1955), 207–11

——. 'Mollusca from limestone in Skye', *J Conchology* 24 (1957), 171–3

Jackson, D. J. 'Notes on Water Beetles from the Island of Raasay', *Scot Nat*, 66 (1954), 30–4

——. 'The capacity for flight of certain water beetles and its bearing on their origin in the western Scottish Isles', *Proc Linn Soc*, 167 (1954), 76–94

Jewell, P. A., Milner, C., Boy, J. M. *Island Survivors* (1974), Athlone Press

Lack, D. 'Ecological Features of the Bird Faunas in British small islands', *J Animal Ecol*, 11 (1942), 9–36

Last, H. 'Beetles from the Outer Hebrides', *Ent Mon Mag*, 109 (1973), 61

Lockie, J. D. and Stephen, D. 'Eagles, Lambs and Land Management on Lewis', *J Animal Ecol*, 28 (1959), 43–50

Loder, J. de V. *Colonsay and Oronsay in the Isles of Argyll* (Edinburgh, 1935)

Luff, M. L. and Davies, L. 'Ecological Observations on some Carabidae from St. Kilda with notes on other beetles new to the island', *Ent Mon Mag*, 108 (1972), 46–51

MacDougall, H. 'Notes on the Birds of Coll', *Scot Nat* (1938), 139–44

Macleod, A. M. 'Some aspects of the plant ecology of the Island of Barra', *Trans Bot Soc Edin*, 35 (1948), 67–81

Macnab, P. A. *The Isle of Mull* (David & Charles, Newton Abbot, 1970)

Matthews, L. Harrison. *British Mammals* (1952 2nd Ed 1960), Collins

Meiklejohn, M. F. M. and Stanford, J. K. 'June Notes on the birds of Islay', *Scot Nat*, 66 (1954), 129–45

Mercer, John. *The Hebridean Islands: Islay, Jura, Colonsay* (Published Glasgow, 1974)

Miller, K. W. and Owen, J. A. 'A List of Insects from the Island of Ulva', *Scot Nat*, 64 (1952), 31–7

Muirhead, C. W. 'Flora of Easdale and the Garvellochs', *Trans Bot Soc Edin*, 39 (1962)

Murray, W. H. *The Islands of Western Scotland* (1973), Eyre Methuen.

Nicol, E. A. T. 'Three rare crabs in the Inner Hebrides', *Scot Nat*, (1939), 1–4

——. 'The brackish-water lochs of North Uist', *Proc Roy Soc Edin*, 56 (1936), 169–95

Ogilvie, M. A. and Booth, C. G. 'An oil spillage on Islay in October, 1969', *Scot Birds*, 6 (1970), 149–53

Peacock, A. D., Smith, E. V. and Davidson, O. F. 'Natural History of South Rona', *Scot Nat* (1934) 113–27, 149–63 (1935), 3–10

Perring, F. H. and Randall, R. E. 'An Annotated Flora of the Monach Isles, Outer Hebrides', *Trans Bot Soc Edin*, 41 (1972), 431–44

Ratcliffe, D. A. 'The Peregrine Population of Gt. Britain in 1971', *Bird Study*, 19 No 3 (1972) 117–56

Rintoul, L. J. and Baxter, E. V. 'Natural History Notes from the Isle of Gigha', *Scot Nat*, 62 (1950), 93–7

Ritchie, W. *The beaches of Barra and the Uists* (Dept of Geog, Aberdeen, published for Countryside Commission of Scotland, 1971)

Ritchie, W. and Mather, A. *The beaches of Lewis and Harris*

(Dept of Geog, Aberdeen, published for Countryside Commission of Scotland, 1970)

Robson, M. and Wills, P. 'Notes on the birds of Bearasay, Lewis', *Scot Birds*, 2 (1963), 410–14

Scottish Mountaineering Club. *The Islands of Scotland* (Edinburgh, 1952)

Sergeant, D. E. and Whidborne, R. F. 'Birds on Mingulay in the summer of 1949', *Scot Nat*, 63 (1951), 8–25

Sillar, F. C. and Meyler, Ruth. *Skye* (David & Charles, Newton Abbot, 1973)

Spence, D. H. N. 'Studies on the Vegetation of Shetland III Scrub in Shetland and in South Uist', *J Ecol*, 48 (1960), 73–95

Statistical Account of Scotland (3rd) Argyllshire (1961)

Steel, W. O. and Woodroffe, G. E. (Ed) 'The Entomology of the Isle of Rhum National Nature Reserve,' *Trans Soc Brit Ent*, 18, Pt 6 (1969), 91–167

Stephen, A. C. 'Notes on the intertidal fauna of North Uist', *Scot Nat* (1935), 137–42

Stephenson, W. 'An Ecological Survey of a beach on the Island of Raasay', *Proc Durham Phil Soc*, 10 (1941), 332–57

Stewart, M. 'Natural History Notes on Scottish Islands', *Scot Nat* (1938), 107–14

Temperley, G. W. 'Notes on the bird life of the island of Raasay', *Scot Nat* (1938), 11–27

Thompson, Francis. *St Kilda and other Hebridean Outliers* (David & Charles, Newton Abbot, 1970)

——. *Harris and Lewis* (David & Charles, Newton Abbot, 1973)

Tremewan, W. G. and Carter, D. G. 'Collecting Zygaena in Scotland in 1966', *Ent Gaz*, 18 (1967), 3–9

Vose, P. B., Powell, H. G., and Spence, J. B. 'The machair grazings of Tiree', *Trans Bot Soc Edin*, 37 (1957), 89–110

Walton, G. A. 'Hebridean Hydrocorisae; general taxonomy', *Trans Roy Ent Soc Lond*, 92 (1942), 417–52

Warwick, T. 'Notes on Mammals of the Isles of Barra, Mingulay and Berneray, Outer Hebrides', *Scot Nat* (1938), 57–9

Weir, T. *The Scottish Lochs* (Constable, 1972)

Welch, R. Colin and Beales, R. W. '*Hermaeophaga mercurialis* and some other Coleoptera from the Outer Hebrides', *Ent*, 101 (1968), 5–7

West, G. 'A comparative study of the dominant phanerogams and higher cryptogram flora of aquatic habit in three lake areas of Scotland', *Proc Roy Soc Edin*, 25 (1905), 967–1023

Whitehead, G. K. *The Deer of Great Britain and Ireland* (1964), Routledge, Kegan & Paul

——. *Wild Goats of Great Britain and Ireland* (David & Charles, Newton Abbot, 1972)

Williamson, K. and Boyd, J. M. *St Kilda Summer* (1960), Hutchinson

——. *A Mosaic of Islands* (1963), Oliver & Boyd

Wormell, P. 'Notes on Lepidoptera of the Isle of Rhum', *Ent*, 95 (1962), 94–6

Acknowledgements

It should be made clear that the term 'Western Isles' as used throughout this book has a wider connotation than the new local government area and refers to the whole region.

The Hebrides are so scattered, remote and numerous that an author is inevitably much dependent on observations and studies made by earlier writers. I acknowledge my indebtedness to such, in particular to the various expeditions made by several universities.

I am grateful to Mr W. A. J. Cunningham of Stornoway and Mr C. G. Booth of Port Ellen for patiently answering certain queries. Nearer home, Mr P. H. Carne, Rear-Admiral Torlesse and Mr P. Bowman have again been of help.

Once again I record my thanks to the library service, especially to the staff of the National Library of Scotland and of the Loans Department of the British Library at Boston Spa who kindly granted me special facilities.

My wife, as always, has assisted me in various ways, neglecting her own writing activity to do so; to her I give my grateful thanks.

Index

Italic figures indicate illustrations

177